Berghof F

The Burning Question

Climate and conflict – why does it matter?

Andrew Gilmour

Preface

My first forays into the world of climate change and conflict – at that time with barely an inkling of the various links between them – were strikingly unsuccessful.

In 2004, while working in the UN regional office for West Africa, it seemed to me that the introduction of cheap solar cookers in the conflict zones of Sierra Leone, Liberia and Côte d'Ivoire would be an obvious solution to several problems. I had been inspired by my next-door neighbour in New York, the great artist Mary Frank, who was keen to promote solar ovens. Such cookers would preserve the trees and other vegetation that were being cut down in mass quantities for firewood, especially in areas that hosted large numbers of refugees from the fighting in neighbouring countries. They would reduce the need for women to travel large distances on foot to collect wood for their cooking fires, many of whom were raped or abducted on their journeys. Respiratory diseases among women and children from daily exposure to smoke while cooking would lessen. And families would no longer need to spend significant portions of their income to buy sacks of charcoal, and would therefore have more resources to spend on health, education or investment in improved agricultural methods.

I placed a model of the cheapest and simplest such cooker in my office – basically cardboard covered in reflective tinfoil that turned into a simple cooking device that even I could manage to put together. I badgered everyone who came to visit me, and promoted it around the region. I had meetings with refugee groups, donors, and with the Association of Women Engineers in Timbuktu – in what later became a terrible conflict zone but at that time was relatively peaceful – we produced a project proposal which I discussed with donor embassies, UN agencies and large NGOs. Abysmally, I did not succeed in generating commitment to fund a single solar cooker in all of West Africa.

My next effort fared no better. Arriving in the UN's Iraq Mission in 2007, at a time when much of the country was embroiled in different conflicts, I contemplated the vast hangar-sized roofs that covered UN premises – for purposes of protection against sun, rain and incoming rocket attacks. If painted white, they could become a superb way to reflect the sun's rays back from the burning heat of the desert and tarmac of Baghdad into the atmosphere – an example of how to resist climate change and global warming, known as 'solar radiation management', that was in vogue at the time. I was fobbed off with lame excuses about frequent dust-storms apparently nullifying the effect of white-painted roofs by covering them with sand, and other bureaucratic reasons to avoid someone having to carry out a task that was 'new' and not explicitly mandated.

But despite these failures, my interest in the topic did not diminish. And indeed I received much inspiration regarding the importance of mitigating climate change from senior UN friends and my bosses. Ahmedou Ould-Abdallah, the head of the UN first in West Africa and later Somalia, was extraordinarily prescient in both places regarding the additional new threats to peace and stability from climate change. Later at UN Headquarters, Secretary-General Ban Ki-Moon and Deputy Secretary-General Jan Eliasson established climate change as arguably the UN's top priority, while Prince Zeid Ra'ad al Hussein promoted it in UN Human Rights. Other colleagues – Jeff Feltman, Valerie Amos, Kyung-wha Kang – also played prominent roles. I appreciate the leadership and support of all.

I am very grateful to the fellows and librarians of All Souls College, Oxford who helped me during my visiting fellowship there in 2021. My biggest debt in this regard is to Edward Mortimer, who not only encouraged me to apply for that All Souls fellowship, but wrote to me after I gave a lecture to the college fellows, urging me to make it "the basis of a short book, which should be published as soon as possible, given the extreme urgency of the issues."

Tragically, Edward died just a few days later. Until he wrote that message, I had not intended to write such a book. I hope he would have approved of the product, although it would undoubtedly have been a finer book had it been able to benefit in draft from his immense wisdom.

Climate change presents a number of threats to security: meaning here the security of individuals, communities, provinces, states, and entire regions. Some of these threats translate more or less into contributory causes of conflict. Without getting into the slightly pointless debate about the precise correlation between rising ambient temperatures and rising human tensions, this book seeks to examine the various linkages between climate and conflict, and the different pathways that exist to turn changes of climate into intensified sources of conflict. These regrettable pathways derive from climate change itself *directly*. But they also derive from measures that people are taking to counter the causes and the effects of altered weather patterns (so, more *indirectly*).

Countries in conflict are often those that are disproportionately affected by climate change (by the greenhouse gases that other, wealthier and less affected countries have emitted). They also receive – precisely because they are in conflict – the smallest quantities of climate finance.

This state of affairs cannot be allowed to continue. The only people who benefit from it are those who seek to profit from violence and instability. Moreover, in the longer run, countries in conflict (or even those associated with it from a distance, as we can see from the fall-out of the Ukraine war) are distracted from the global necessity of taking action against climate change, to the detriment of everyone.

Admittedly the topic of this book is not exactly an uplifting one. If reading about the impact of climate change can be depressing enough on its own, combining it with its effect on conflict may seem almost gratuitously gloom-laden. For me, and I hope a growing number of others, the number one burning question is to consider how best to understand and then respond to the many, varied links between climate and conflict. Failing to do so adequately will have catastrophic results.

At the Berghof Foundation in Berlin, where I became Executive Director in 2020, I am grateful to the Board and its chair, Johannes Zundel, who supported my recommendation to bring climate change into the heart of Berghof's work on conflict transformation, as well as to several colleagues there who have embraced that change with great enthusiasm and skill. The German Foreign Office has recently begun to fund our climate-related work in conflict areas in Africa and the Middle East, while the foreign ministries of Finland, Norway, and Switzerland have generously provided core funding to Berghof, including for the costs of this publication.

A number of friends and peers have reviewed and sent extremely helpful comments on drafts of this book. These include Adam Parr, Natasha Hall, Shirin Reuvers, Johnny West, Archie Gilmour, Hillary Crowe, Hugo Dixon, Carne Ross, Ngozi Amu, Beatrix Austin, Janine di Giovanni, Joya Rajadhyaksha, Janani Vivekananda, Anthony Cardon de Lichtbuer, Emma Williams Gilmour, Jay Collins, Annett Rößling, Natalie Baharav, Alexander Reiffenstuel, Janel Galvanek and Eleanor Beevor.

My deepest thanks go to Tom Breese, who, since he started at Berghof in 2021, has carried out research on climate-related issues, proved an exceptionally able colleague and helped in many ways to put this book together.

Andrew Gilmour
Berlin, November 2023

1 Introduction

Reality often dawns slowly. For the far-sighted few, this is naturally cause for profound frustration. In the near and distant past, there have been numerous examples of communities and governments which, faced with threats of varying nature and gravity, have delayed confronting them.

In his magisterial global history of humankind's interaction with our environment published shortly before this study was finalised, Peter Frankopan has concluded that much of human history has been about "the failure to understand or adapt to changes in the physical and natural world around us, and about the consequences that ensue."[1] Decisive steps to adapt or mitigate the extent of the threat are frequently taken too late to stave off disaster.

It is now increasingly accepted – although there is still a long way to go when confronted with science denialist campaigns, fossil-fuel lobbies, populist politicians and the conservative media – that climate change is the issue that will define humanity's future. The changes witnessed in dangerous weather patterns and rising temperatures and sea levels have been relatively limited to date, compared to what is likely to come, even if the resulting losses have been devastating for those affected. Increasing extremes in every manifestation of climate change are to be expected in the decade to come, with trends predicted to get even worse as the century progresses. In July 2023, as heat records were again being broken from Arizona to Umbria to Xinjiang, as well as in the oceans, UN Secretary-General António Guterres announced "the era of global warming has ended; the era of global boiling has arrived."[2]

Amidst the parallel crises of biodiversity and pollution,[i] we have already seen an increase of 1.1°C, as well as a dramatic increase in the frequency of extreme weather events: catastrophic floods as those in Pakistan in 2022, and heatwaves surpassing 45°C on several continents that same year.[ii] Arctic ice sheets have receded on average by almost a third since the 1990s.[6] And still emissions continue to rise, with another 37 gigatonnes of carbon dioxide released into the atmosphere in 2022 alone.[7]

The climate crisis affects almost every aspect of personal, public, social, natural and economic life. The UN High Commissioner for Human Rights declared that "the world has never seen a threat to

---

i Rapid biodiversity loss similarly has repercussions on human security. It can be mitigated by successful conservation efforts, which, when combined with peacebuilding activities, can support peaceful social, economic, and environmental restoration even in areas affected by conflict.[3] As biodiversity loss and pollution continue to keep pace with climate change, the need for combined action is immense, and while not the explicit focus in this book, the lessons from environmental peacebuilding (see Chapter 7) may well be transferred to conservation practices, to ensure that the latter do not inadvertently contribute to conflict (a principle often referred to in development and peacebuilding circles as "do no harm"). Similarly, it is essential that efforts to address one environmental challenge, even climate change, do not come by creating others. So, the drive to reduce emissions has to avoid damaging ecosystems and habitats on land or in the water, a point recently made from a seemingly unlikely source, Henry Paulson, the former head of Goldman Sachs and Secretary of the Treasury under US President George Bush, in an article entitled "We must stop climate solutions from killing biodiversity."[4]

ii In an attempt to quantify the disaster that we are now in, 28 scientists led by Johann Rockström identified the nine processes which regulate and stabilise the earth system. For each of these processes, they found a threshold beyond which the risk of generating large-scale abrupt or irreversible environmental changes massively increases - known as the 'planetary boundaries'. We have now exceeded six of these interlinked boundaries, of which climate change is just one. Together with land-system change, biodiversity loss, biogeochemical flows, freshwater change and release of novel entities, climate change is creating an ecological crisis of multiple dimensions.[5]

human rights of this scope."[i] [9] The impact of that threat will also be felt in the connected areas of peace, security and conflict. The Director of the US Central Intelligence Agency, William Burns, sees equal cause for alarm: "We can no longer talk about 'tipping points' and 'catastrophic climate impacts' in the future tense. They are here and now, imperilling our planet, our security, our economies and our people... Climate change is the quintessential 'threat multiplier' – fuelling energy, health, water and food insecurities, setting back our progress on economic and human development, turbocharging what is already the worst period of forced displacement and migration in history, and further exacerbating instability and geopolitical tensions and flash points." [10]

Environmental history is a recent discipline – even most historians were barely aware of its existence just 40 years ago. It has been described

---

i An entire book could be written on the linkages between climate change and human rights. Indeed, the present author has carried out a fair amount of research on the topic, but this is not that book. The environmental and human rights movements have historically often worked more in opposition to one another than in partnership, despite being natural allies with common enemies (after all, human rights abusers are often also climate change deniers or environmental despoilers). Fortunately, this is beginning to change. But in a seminal report in 2019, Philip Alston, a UN Special Rapporteur on human rights, castigated the human rights community for its failure to face up to the fact that "human rights may not survive the coming upheaval." The idea that democratic systems failed to prevent global heating may well take hold, with a resulting urge to strengthen state powers at the cost of rights and freedoms.[8]

At the risk of simplifying, the human rights movement first began to appreciate the intersection between human rights and the environment via the impact of the harmful effects on people from pollution. Then, interest was increased in light of the numbers of environmental human rights activitists who were killed while confronting polluting corporations and their supportive governments. It took longer for most human rights organizations to see climate change as the massive threat it poses to rights everywhere.

The links between human rights violations and conflict are increasingly understood, with such violations now recognised not just as a symptom of conflict, but also as a cause. There are many three-way connections between climate, conflict and human rights. Although environmentalists and human rights advocates are working together more effectively than they used to, tensions still flare up, including leading up to the 2022 COP27 in Egypt, a country where extensive rights violations have been both a cause and an effect of conflict. Environmental groups like Greenpeace were accused by rights groups of "greenwashing" the Egyptian government and downplaying its record (including imprisonment, torture and even death sentences handed out to environmental rights defenders). It is indeed the case that, for climate change action to be successful, it requires a vibrant civil society with human rights activists who can hold governments and corporations to account. In that sense, advocates of both climate change action and human rights protection have a case when they point out that of the two emergencies currently faced – human rights and climate change – the first is the most important one, because without rights and freedoms, there is no chance of pressurising those responsible to reduce emissions.

as an attempt to analyse how "nature and culture blur together" (or, more prosaically, how to "combine science and the humanities") and show that the environment's impact on society cannot be divorced from existing power structures and social divisions.[11] Few of this discipline's leading exponents have so far delved deeply into the environment's interactions with human conflict.[i]

Even so, there have been some convincing attempts to explain conflict and societal disintegration in the face of changes in climate. One example was the book *Collapse* by Jared Diamond (2005) which showed how a number of societies (the Maya in the 8th and 9th centuries CE, the Norse of Greenland and the Assyrians as far back as the 7th and 6th centuries BCE) fell apart when significant climate change was combined with factors such as hostile neighbours, natural resource shortages and cultural inflexibility.[12]

Another example is Geoffrey Parker's vast study of the global crisis in the 17th century and the links he made between war, catastrophe and climate change connected to the Little Ice Age. As Parker puts it, that century "experienced extremes of weather seldom witnessed before and never (so far) since".[13] He firmly linked the political turbulence and conflict in large parts of Europe, Asia and elsewhere during that period with the climate change being experienced at that time. The fallout included the collapse of the Ming dynasty, the Thirty Years War, and the English Civil War, all in mid-century.[ii]

---

i The same is true of *climate history*, which focuses on how societies have been affected by climate (as opposed to *historical climatology*, which is the scientific study of climate data from previous centuries).

ii On a personal note, the present writer was an undergraduate in history at Oxford in the 1980s, studying such topics as the Thirty Years War and the English Civil War. These examples of 17th century conflict were presented by historians with no reference to the climate change that societies were undergoing. What I do not recall ever reading (and as a Scot I would have remembered) was that between 1637 and 1649, Scotland suffered the longest drought in its recorded history, combined with searingly cold winters. And the misery this caused was clearly a contributory factor in the invasion of England by a Scots army in 1640.[14] But it should be noted that there were three major differences between the climate changes of the 17th and 21st centuries: i) the planet was getting colder not hotter; ii) the change was not man-made; iii) and it was only a one-degree change, as opposed to the far higher increases we are currently on track to experiencing. Similarly, it has been suggested that over three centuries earlier in Scotland, climate issues – cold winters and wet summers, leading to food shortages – played a role in heightening anti-English sentiment and support for William Wallace's rebellion for independence in the 1290s.

Other historians have suggested that the El Niño climate event of 1788-95 contributed to drought and famine in Africa and India, as well as to the French Revolution (and, therefore, the Napoleonic wars that followed over the next two decades); and that climate variability was a factor in the weakening of both the Ottoman and Spanish Empires (especially the uprisings in Mexico in 1810).[15] Studies have also linked weather and climate to the persecution of minorities. It has been shown that over a 700-year period, even small drops in temperature, when they led to food shortages, increased the probability of attacks against Jews in Europe. Similarly, Christians in Egypt suffered when the Nile failed to provide enough water for irrigation. And large numbers of women in 15th and 16th century Europe were accused of witchcraft, tortured and burned, often as scapegoats for poor harvests that resulted from climate change.[16]

In none of the above examples has climate change been put forward as the sole cause of the conflicts concerned. But these historians have produced a compelling case that among the other factors responsible for the outbreak or intensification of conflict – political, social, cultural, economic or human rights-related – climate change was also a contributor.

This is also the case with the 'new', mainly intra-state, wars of the post-Cold War era. While there is vigorous debate in academic and conflict analyst circles about its precise causal effect on contemporary conflict, the general consensus is that climate change does play a contributory role, and that this is likely to increase as the climate crisis itself intensifies.

The reasons for this linkage between climate and conflict are complex and vary from place to place, although there are also some broad common patterns.[i] Climate change tends to put extra pressure on communities that are already fragile (because they live either in countries where conflict has become endemic, or else in areas that are economically under-developed, both factors resulting in a vulnerability that means they are less able to cope) by damaging the environment in which they live

---

i Most of the observations that follow in the next two paragraphs could apply in some form to many of the conflicts in the Sahel, the Horn of Africa, North Africa, the Middle East and Central Asia.

and work. This may make some vital resources – such as water or farmland – extremely scarce and worsen the quality of life to the point where deaths occur.

This pressure can expose vulnerabilities in communities, lead to tensions and competition in the struggle to survive, and thereby heighten the risk of serious violence. In areas beset by conflict, weak institutions lack the means to help communities adapt to climate pressure, or to prevent others from carrying out activities that compound it. Armed groups, for instance in the Sahel or the Middle East, may take control of – and weaponise – scarce resources. Marginalised groups in society are more vulnerable in such times of stress, and this may increase the rate of gender-based violence or discrimination against minorities. Where the pressure (as a combination of environmental, political and social factors) becomes unbearable, migration may appear to be the only option. This puts additional stress on the migrating population, as well as on local communities in areas to which they move. Each of these effects of climate change and other environmental pressures increases the risk of conflict.

But it is not just the impact of climate change *itself* that is likely to fuel conflict. How we all (at international, national, state or community level) *respond to* climate change will also generate risk. Some important actions taken to mitigate climate change are likely to have an unplanned, indirect impact that increases tensions and conflict. For instance, several governments – Iraq, Nigeria, and Russia are three – that are heavily dependent on revenue from fossil fuels (especially oil) have structured their economies in such an undiversified way that the global exit from fossil fuels is likely to leave their finances dangerously exposed. Managing such a transition to more renewable sources of energy in ways that minimise the risks of violence will involve losers as well as beneficiaries at all levels. This will be particularly difficult in countries that are already affected by recent or current conflict.

Whether direct or indirect (i.e. whether it is from climate change itself, or rather as an unintended consequence of our responses to it), the impact of climate change on fragile and conflict-affected countries is certain to spill over national borders, probably leading to vastly greater numbers needing to migrate from the worst-affected areas. Even if most of those displaced by climate change have hitherto remained in their own country or region, people will feel compelled to move further afield as temperatures continue to rise and as nearby options run out of capacity to host them.

Climate change is expected to make a number of regions even more inhospitable or indeed uninhabitable, due to a variety of factors: rising sea levels causing land submergence; salinisation of farmland and the aquifers used for irrigation; increasingly destructive extreme weather events; wildfires; devastating droughts; floods; famine; or heat levels that the human body simply cannot cope with.

There is also the relatively unexplored but serious risk of vicious cycles. The effects of climate change, described above, increase the risk of conflict in various ways, not least by creating incentives for some people and compelling others to join armed groups which commit further violence. This intensified level of conflict, in turn, can cause further environmental degradation while impeding climate change mitigation efforts (to reduce emissions) and the adaptation measures required to enable communities to cope with climate change.[i]

Creating resilience to these risks must be the guiding principle for all climate and security responses. The provision of support for conflict-affected areas — so that they can adapt physically, socially and economically to such risks — is essential. But adapting to this new reality requires significant investment to create climate-resilient infrastructure, living conditions and economic opportunities. The existing climate finance system is utterly failing in this regard. Currently, inhabitants in the most fragile and conflict-affected areas are receiving just over one per cent of climate finance per capita relative to those living in non-fragile states.[17] Whether this is due to the unstable political and military environments, to the lack of financial incentives to encourage investment, or a combination of the two, it is the

---

i This can take place at both global and local levels. In the case of the latter, it is of course even harder to raise investments, given the clear risks that conflict presents to potential investors, to enable local communities to adapt to climate change when they live in areas vulnerable to conflict. Globally, following the Russian invasion of Ukraine in February 2022, the debate against fossil fuels was immediately put on the backburner as countries rushed to increase their supplies of oil, gas and coal, even to the extent of re- opening coal mines.

most vulnerable areas of the planet that receive the least support for their efforts to adapt to climate change. This makes little sense and can hardly be in anyone's long-term interest.[i]

Notwithstanding the mass of scientific evidence spelling likely catastrophe, as well as the nice-sounding but wholly inadequate and unfulfilled pledges made by senior government figures at COP meetings, global greenhouse gas emissions are still increasing. Because of the greenhouse gases already in the atmosphere, temperatures are going to continue to rise, even once emission levels are brought down. Thus, it will no longer be possible to reduce climate-related security risks solely through the current level of climate *mitigation* measures. Such measures are of course essential, but for many communities they can only limit the damage.

At the same time, therefore, we also need large-scale, targeted *adaptation* measures to reduce the security threats that accompany climate change. As we will see, these are not mutually exclusive: measures such as improving agricultural methods or renewable projects can contribute to both mitigation and adaptation.

Currently, climate-related funding is biased toward mitigation, and adaptation draws the short end of the stick. Adaptation projects are often less attractive to the private sector which tends to steer well clear of them, putting the onus directly on grants and loans from richer countries. But even official development assistance and multilateral development bank funds fall far short of what is necessary to address the social, economic, humanitarian needs of adaptation, much less to address the resulting security issues simmering below the surface.

There are, however, various important reasons for richer countries to reduce overall climate-related security risks by investing in adaptation measures in the developing world, including in those countries facing forms

i It is not in anybody's long-term interest. But it may well be in the short-term interest of those who profit — commercially or geopolitically — from conflict, such as President Putin or the Wagner Group, before the demise of its leader, Yevgeny Prigozhin. Other beneficiaries may include far-right candidates and parties in Western countries who proclaim that they are "anti-immigrant" but secretly all know they benefit electorally when people are forced to flee from the effects of climate change or conflict and seek refuge in countries with more liveable climes.

of armed conflict that fall short of actual war. In the pages that follow, a number of those reasons will be addressed. Some are self-interested ones, others are more principled, relating to 'climate justice'. Low levels of economic development are frequently a contributory cause of conflict. However, it is also partly a result of not having engaged in carbon-emitting activities in the past. This was usually because the previously colonised countries concerned were never in a position – and perhaps were never intended by those who ruled them to be in such a position – to profit from any type of industrial revolution.

The result is a bitter irony for numerous vulnerable countries. Colonisation should not of course be blamed for every shortcoming and deprivation suffered in the developing world. But it is nevertheless the case that having colonised much of the globe and denied other peoples such development paths that they themselves enjoyed through their use of fossil fuels, those same developed countries are asking Africa and other low-income countries to pursue 'green industrialisation' pathways without providing them the funding to do so. In fact, in the poorest developing countries – many of which are in Africa, whose continental emissions amount to at most four per cent of the global total – the issue they face is not the energy "transition away" from anything.

The real issue is to obtain enough foreign investment in green power and energy to enable them to industrialise in the first place. Otherwise, we must all face the reality that investing in fossil fuel will be the way to go for the under-developed countries, at least until they are in a position to access funds for green industrialisation instead.

The countries in this situation have not only played a negligible role in emitting the carbon that has accumulated in the atmosphere. In addition – since they are often the states worst hit by climate change – they will be the ones most likely to experience conflicts as a result. On top of all that, they are the least able to finance and carry out sizeable adaptation measures for their own populations.

It would be quite wrong to caricature calls for climate justice as 'radical leftist' or 'anti-Western'. Rather, climate justice should be embraced as the means of reducing both global inequality and planetary collapse. Moreover, this is likely to become the dominant narrative of international discourse in the coming years, and continued failure to respond to the concerns of poorer countries will widen the divide between developed 'Northern' (or 'Western') and developing 'Southern' nations. As has been seen with the war in Ukraine (and will be explored in the penultimate chapter of this book), this division creates a strategic opportunity for countries like Russia to exploit. Self-interest and moral responsibility converge very conveniently on this point.

Discussion of climate change, conflict and security has centred on many of the above issues, recognising how climate change negatively impacts peace and security as well as so much else. At the inter-state level, a good example of a major threat posed by climate change to peace and security is the massive Grand Ethiopian Renaissance Dam (GERD). While the issue encompasses important development, agricultural and military factors, it is at its heart an environmental dispute between three countries (Egypt, Sudan, and Ethiopia), each of which believes, with good reason, that the flow of the Nile is existential for them. What makes the situation even more serious – especially in view of Egypt's threats to attack the dam,[i] which would likely lead to full-scale war with Ethiopia – is that climate change is expected to reduce rainfall to the extent that there is simply not going to be enough water to satisfy the needs of all three countries' fast-growing populations.

No major war has ever erupted mainly because of water disputes. But links between water and conflict (as between climate change, which clearly affects water quantities, and conflict) are hard to ignore. As has recently been pointed out, "riparian countries are increasingly involved in each other's ongoing conflicts. Upstream countries have also taken advantage of weakened and conflict-affected riparian states." It is not just Ethiopia that has built a major dam when downstream countries were shaken by unrest. Turkey has similarly taken advantage of strife in Iraq and Syria to withhold its agreed allocations of water from the Euphrates. The resulting lack of cooperation has then contributed to less efficient water management and to rising political tensions, both domestically and internationally.[19]

---

i In 2013, President Morsi of Egypt convened a high-level meeting to discuss the GERD. It did not go quite as planned because those attending had not been informed that the meeting would be televised live, and some of them blithely specified how they would go about bombing the dam or sending special forces to blow it up.[18]

There is a geopolitical angle to the climate-conflict nexus, though not a very direct one. For instance, during G20 climate negotiations in July 2023, Chinese diplomats were accused by representatives from other nations of using aggressive wrecking tactics and blocking discussions on greenhouse gas emission targets. Similarly, there is increasing likelihood that there will be tensions and even conflict over the rare earths that are essential for producing renewable energy and electric vehicles (far more so than for their fossil fuel alternatives), with China using its great leverage in this field – first exercised against Japan as early as 2010 – against its political opponents. As one financial publication put it, "the most pressing concern here is that the very materials which offer optimism for our future could turn the world into a pit of geopolitical tension."[20]

But analysis of the conflict-climate change nexus has focused more on violence within states. While alarm is now being raised about the growing urgency of the question, including at high political levels, efforts to address it remain relatively thin on the ground. The aim of this short book is to analyse conditions and methods for contemplating action in this relatively neglected space. It explains some of the history, and the most relevant and also most contested concepts behind 'climate security' (Chapter 2). The book examines how the links between climate and conflict can be made more harmful or less by human decisions and institutions, especially relating to governance (Chapter 3).

Migration (which is caused both by conflict and by climate change, and in turn can be both an adaptive coping mechanism as well as an added cause of new further conflict) is an increasingly important factor in the entire climate debate. For this reason, there is a discussion of the issues surrounding it (Chapter 4).

There is clearly significant potential for climate change to make conflict more frequent, intense and complicated. Conflict can therefore be seen as a direct impact of climate change; but it also has a more indirect impact in various ways. One of these lies in the measures that individuals, communities and governments take in response to climate change: whether to mitigate emissions or to adapt livelihoods and infrastructures to lessen the hardships that result from change to the climate. This is why this book covers some of the risks implicit in the crucial energy transition away from fossil fuels, as well as the potential of renewable energy systems at the local level, including in areas of conflict (Chapter 5).

The next two chapters look more closely at what can be done to reduce these risks. The first (Chapter 6) explores climate adaptation as a strategy to overcome climate vulnerability in conflict areas, and the second (Chapter 7) looks at how this can be supported by environmental peacebuilding as a distinct but related approach. Together, they draw on examples from many regions in the world to highlight opportunities to simultaneously foster peace and environmental resilience.

The penultimate chapter focuses on the war in Ukraine. This is not just because it is the most geopolitically significant violent conflict under way at the time of publication. The main reason is that it illustrates numerous links between climate, environment and conflict on so many levels, both direct and indirect, and thereby also the complexity of the subject with which we will all increasingly need to grapple (Chapter 8).

The final section (Chapter 9) tries to draw together the threads discussed in the book, as well as to suggest some ways to reduce the impact of what appears to be a major impending crisis for much of the world's population. The Conclusions section has been designed as a stand-alone section, emphasising some of the more important points from the preceding sections, but also introducing some new elements when it comes to proposing avenues towards solutions.

This book is not about climate mitigation and the reduction of emissions. Instead, it focuses mainly on how climate change and conflict combine to make adaptation strategies even more necessary, especially in areas that have witnessed serious conflict in recent decades. Just in case it needs saying, there is absolutely no intention by the author to downplay the cardinal importance of mitigation, principally by drastically cutting the use of fossil fuels. It is just that when looking at the nexus of climate change and conflict, it seems clear that the adaptation side of the debate is of even greater relevance, especially in countries barely responsible for any greenhouse gas emissions but suffering most from the impact of the emissions from others.

2 Climate and security: how perceptions are shifting

Since the early 1990s, the issue of climate change has become increasingly embedded in narratives of security. Many states, intergovernmental institutions and NGOs have acknowledged, to varying degrees, the importance of addressing the security implications of climate change. Even so, after three decades of discussions, there has been little practical action to show for it, although this has started to change. For a long time, a lack of consensus on the nature and even the existence of climate-related security risks has made it hard for decision-making bodies to address them. Even where they have chosen to bring together these issues, their efforts remain at the initial stages.[21]

Precisely to whom a changing climate is likely to pose a particular and acute threat is a question which has made coalition-building on the topic so hard. Whether it is assessed as a threat to nation states, to the international order, or to the wellbeing of communities or even individuals, the perception of climate change can produce very different kinds of responses.[22]

At least from 1965, when the White House published its first assessment of global warming, there was some discussion of climate change and its potential harmful effects, including rising sea levels, ocean acidification and loss of agricultural productivity, as well as its link to fossil fuels and emissions.[23] But oddly as it seems today, the aspect emphasised in some other quarters was that climate change could lead to global *cooling*, because particles from emissions would block the sun's rays on the surface of the planet. However, the first major effort to reduce the use of fossil fuel was triggered not by fears of climate change (cooling or heating), but by the effects of the Yom Kippur War in 1973, after which the Arab states imposed an oil embargo on the US and Israel and massively increased the price of oil. By the late 1970s, according to the US Secretary of Defense, "the present deficiency of assured energy sources is the single surest threat ... to our security and to that of our allies."[24]

Within a few years, the consensus became that the impact of fossil fuel emissions would lead not to planetary cooling, but rather its opposite. The link to conflict was also increasingly acknowledged. At the 1988 Toronto Conference on the Changing Atmosphere, delegates concluded that the unintended consequences of human activities could be "second only to a global nuclear war".[25] In 1991, the topic was inserted into the US National Security Strategy under the George H. W. Bush administration, which came to see the enormity of climate change as turning into a national security threat with the potential to undermine America's global influence and strategic operations. Set against the backdrop of the invasion of Kuwait, where departing Iraqi forces had set ablaze over 600 oil wells, and with the growing momentum that led to the 1992 Earth Summit in Rio, it is little surprise that the two very different spheres of environment and defence had begun to overlap by this point.

At the same time, the Canadian scholar Thomas Homer-Dixon published an article titled "On the Threshold: Environmental Changes as Causes of Acute Conflict". Through this piece, Homer-Dixon became one of the first to identify the link between environmental factors and the causes of conflict. Admitting the vast array of implications of climate change and environmental degradation, he narrowed his research to what he called "acute national and international conflict."[26] As one of the earliest pieces of academic research on this topic, it was understandable for him to focus on what seemed the most politically salient connections – between environmental change and national and international conflict. But to many readers with less knowledge of the topic, it provided a too constricted lens through which to see environmental issues – as threats to international and national security.

Momentum continued to build and three years later, in an article titled "The Coming Anarchy", Robert Kaplan warned of the perils of environmental scarcity. Indeed, he went further than Homer-Dixon, claiming in no uncertain terms: "It is time to understand the environment for what it is: the national security issue of the early twenty-first century."[27] This article and its thesis continued to gain traction in policy circles and was recommended reading in President Bill Clinton's White House.[28]

By 2003, the issue of climate and refugees had reached the Pentagon, by then starting to become immersed in the two 'quagmires' of Iraq and Afghanistan. Despite the US administration being staffed with many climate change deniers, from President George W. Bush downwards, the Department of Defense commissioned a report entitled "An Abrupt Climate Change Scenario and Its Implications for United States National Security".[29] It warned that a changing climate would lead to "skirmishes, battles and even war" and highlighted the new threat it posed to US national security. It also suggested that some states should bolster their border control strategies to keep out people displaced by weather events.[30] Whether inadvertently or not, this strategy advocated for barriers to be put up against those most vulnerable to climate change – reflecting the tendency to view climate change through the narrow prism of national security, with little consideration for the lives and livelihoods of people of other nationalities. The obvious downside of approaching climate security in this way is that it becomes too easy for people waving the patriotic flag to present the 'solutions' in terms of building walls, raising drawbridges and capsizing dinghies.

Elsewhere, the US Department of Defense also set out to 'climate proof' its military bases overseas, shoring up its own strategic positions and global interests. In recent years, the US has identified that 1,774 of its military bases will be subjected to sea-level rise.[31] The inundation of these bases would obviously reduce their usefulness as launch pads for military operations and, so the thinking went, would thus undermine the 'existing global order'. Indeed, the cause of this sea- level rise has also prompted concerns about a new strategic military environment and the international security architecture.

Temperatures in the Arctic are warming nearly four times faster than the global average.[32] Alongside this temperature increase comes rapid ice melt, with new channels for trade and natural resource extraction opening up – along with opportunities for sabotage of undersea cables, espionage, blockade of sea lanes and military build-up. The scramble for access by Russia, the US, several European states, and China (with the last planning a 'Polar Silk Road') has potential to increase tensions between powers with significant military arsenals, with comparisons being made to a new Arctic version of the 19th century 'Great Game' that had played out between the British and Russian Empires in Central Asia. More civilian, commercial and military activity will increase the probability of misunderstandings and accidents, particularly in the absence of strong and capable Arctic governance institutions.[33] Indeed, since the Russian invasion of Ukraine, activities in the Arctic Council (an institution supposed to promote cooperation including on issues relating to climate change) have been put on hold because seven of its members decided they could no longer work with the eighth, Russia.[34]

With geopolitical tensions rising (and militaries expanding), the conversation is also turning to how the increase in the size of security forces and defence spending is driving up emissions globally. Governments have ramped up military capacities across Western Europe and beyond. For the first time, annual global military expenditures have surpassed US$2 trillion.[35] Whatever one's stance on this, it is undeniable that it will make it even more difficult to keep global warming below 1.5°C. The US military alone is estimated to have a greater level of emissions than most nation states.[i] If it were a single

---

i In 2017, the Pentagon's emissions exceeded those of Sweden, Denmark and Portugal.[36]

country, it would be the world's 47th largest emitter.[37] Other defence establishments also emit at high levels. Indeed, military infrastructure substantially depends on the energy created from fossil fuels which, as former CIA director David Petraeus put it in a memo to US forces in Afghanistan in 2011, are "the lifeblood of our warfighting capabilities".[38] So, the current trend of increased militarisation poses yet another impediment to reducing emissions.

This does not mean that military thinking is disinclined to come up with solutions. Indeed, in some circumstances, the opposite may be true. Although it dates from relatively early days of military awareness of these dangers, and thinking has progressed further since then, the following example is helpful. During the US invasion and occupation of Iraq, the writer Thomas Friedman was struck by what he called the "green hawks" movement in the military that emerged in 2006. Delivering huge quantities of diesel fuel to US bases, mainly for air-conditioning inside tents for the US marines in parts of the country such as Anbar province, was an especially perilous assignment because of roadside bombs. The obvious solution for reducing such journeys was to use renewable energy instead of diesel fuel. Thus began what Friedman termed the army's first comprehensive attempt at "out- greening al-Qaeda" – trying to chip away at al-Qaeda's advantage of being a dispersed guerrilla force requiring few energy resources confronting a concentrated high-energy consuming conventional army, by looking for green solutions. One US energy logistician declared that if he were to tell his commander he needed solar mirrors and windmills, the reaction would not be positive. "But if I tell him that I have a system of supplementing his convention power with renewables that will give him more tactical flexibility, he will be more comfortable with that idea." The result was that the US military began to use wind turbines and sun-tracking solar panels to power their bases in Iraq. Friedman envisaged these troops returning to their homes in the US and demanding similar solutions in their communities, thereby kick-starting a crucial change in thinking in the US overall.[39] The fact that, 15 years after publication of his book, such a development has been far slower than one would have hoped does not negate the potentially catalytic role that the military can play. Nevertheless, however beneficial the effects of this might be overall, the thinking motivating such a change was clearly in the domain of 'hard' security.

Outside defence ministries and military planning circles, the conversation around climate change and security has often been framed quite differently. Low- lying island states have been facing a national security threat of a very different kind. To countries such as the Maldives, with more than 1,000 islands and atolls less than two metres above sea level, any climate change-induced sea-level rise is an existential threat – a phrase often used by representatives of states, but perhaps never more accurately than in this instance. Given the obvious futility of military responses in such circumstances, these nation states have used other means to raise their concerns.

In 1990, the Alliance of Small Island States was formed to amplify their voices in global debates on climate change, and has since been one of the most vocal advocates for change. Consider the address by Tuvalu's Foreign Minister to the COP26 plenary, delivered standing knee-deep in the ocean, or the powerful advocacy of Barbados' Prime Minister Mia Mottley. For them, framing climate change in terms of national security makes eminent sense. Moreover, even though such arguments stem from national security concerns, they do not have to lead to military-enforced isolationism; leaders like this know that dealing with climate risks does not necessitate taking actions that are detrimental to other countries. The contrasting haste with which many of the larger powers are willing to close their borders and defend a narrowly defined self-interest implies quite substantial risks to others.

In 1994, the UNDP Human Development Report for the first time developed the concept of 'human security'. The aim was to refocus the object of security away from states and towards the well-being of individuals.[i] This wellbeing includes categories such as food

---

i This move was made, according to McDonald, for two reasons: "First, that states are at best unreliable in providing security for their citizens, and in some cases directly undermine the wellbeing of their own populations. Second, that the realities of contemporary global politics are such that a focus on the preservation of state sovereignty and territory no longer reflects the security concerns of most people or the nature of contemporary security challenges."[40]

security, economic security, political security, and human rights; it stresses individuals' entitlement to "freedom from fear and freedom from want, with an equal opportunity to enjoy all their rights and fully develop their human potential".[41]

This distinction is also interesting on other levels. All too often, anything to do with 'security' is perceived as being intrinsically negative, as in securing oneself from some physical threat which needs to be deterred. This can involve a range of mechanisms, from guard dogs to aircraft carriers. And it is here that the human security approach can provide some advances, based on the assumption that what needs to be 'secured' is not just a national border or an individual's physical integrity *from* being aggressed by someone else, but the ability *to* maintain one's way of life with dignity.

This new approach to security, negative or positive – or human security versus national security – can be seen as roughly analogous to the negative and positive liberty set out by the philosopher Isaiah Berlin in his inaugural lecture at Oxford in 1958. Both sets of liberties – the freedom *from* constraints and the freedom *to* be able to do certain things – are perhaps equally important, and the distinction between the two has found its way into human rights discourse, with 'negative' civil and political rights on the one hand,[i] and 'positive' economic, social, and cultural rights on the other.[ii]

It is tempting to believe that as the threat of climate change becomes even more acute, there will be greater agreement not only on the nature of the threat, but also on what needs to be done to confront it. And while both forms of security are equally important in many respects, when it comes to climate change, understanding the issues with an eye to human security allows for a much more accurate picture of its full impact. One of the reasons for this is that in many places where the effects of climate change are acute, the state is relatively absent.

---

i Such as the rights to freedom from torture and arbitrary arrest, and the right to practise the religion of one's choice, enjoy freedom of speech or join the political party of one's choice.

ii Such as the rights to access to health and education; or even just the human right to "have breakfast", as the first President of Senegal, Leopold Senghor, once memorably put it.

In the Sahel, temperatures are predicted to rise between 2.0 °C and 4.3°C by 2080 according to Intergovernmental Panel on Climate Change (IPCC) estimates.[42] But in this region, unlike in more developed countries where there are state structures that can respond to climate change, it is at community rather than at state level that a response needs to be made. Communities are left to fend for themselves both to adapt to climate change and also to resolve the conflicts that are exacerbated by it. So it is in regions such as this where, as a key UN official in West Africa, Ngozi Amu, has put it, "a greater burden is placed on the individual, both as a victim of climate change challenges and as a first responder to them."[43]

The framing of climate change as a threat to human security has slowly been gaining currency, particularly within the UN sphere, and in 2007 the issue of climate change reached the UN Security Council. That first debate, proposed by the UK, opened a high-level conversation on the destabilising effects of climate change. While it did not produce any tangible outcomes (not a particularly rare occurrence when the Security Council is involved), it did pave the way for the series of debates at the UN on climate change and security that have taken place since then.[i] The draft resolution put to the Security Council by Ireland and Niger in December 2021 proposed integrating consideration of climate change risks into all aspects of UN programming. It recognised that climate change can lead to social tensions, thereby "exacerbating, prolonging, or contributing to the risk of future conflicts and instability", and proposed integrating "climate-related security risk as a central component into comprehensive conflict-prevention strategies". This perspective encouraged attention to be paid to areas especially vulnerable to climate change. Such an approach was markedly different from the earlier one whereby richer states seemed to think the only effective way to defend themselves against the fall-out of climate insecurity was to forcibly prevent or discourage immigration by desperate victims of rising temperatures, extreme weather and intensified conflict.

---

i The first signs of this tendency to frame climate and security in human security terms can be seen in 2009, in the Secretary-General's report to the General Assembly, the first section of which is titled "Threats to human well-being".[44]

Notwithstanding (or, perhaps, partly because of) this progress, the Council failed to adopt the draft resolution: Russia used its veto, India voted against, and China abstained. The Russian representative argued that the Security Council was the wrong place to discuss climate change because it risked shifting the "attention from genuine deep-rooted reasons for conflict in some countries on the agenda".[45] His Indian counterpart claimed that the draft resolution sought to "obfuscate a lack of progress on critical issues under the UNFCCC process".[46]

Although the votes against the resolution were generally – and not without reason – regarded as motivated by cynicism and a blow to progress on climate issues, not all the criticisms levelled by both representatives were without merit. It is indeed important to ensure that an emphasis on the role of climate change should not provide an excuse for governments whose own policies and decisions lie at the heart of the conflicts they are involved in.

The Russian argument was apparently taking aim at ideas that had first been aired by UN Secretary-General Ban Ki-moon in 2007.[i] In an article about the conflict in Darfur in *The Washington Post*, he suggested that amidst all the other diverse social and political causes, the conflict also "began as an ecological crisis, arising at least in part from climate change", which had led to failing rains and "the essential dilemma – the fact that there's no longer enough good land to go around".[47] At the time, this article sparked fierce disagreement on whether climate factors were being used as a scapegoat for, or a diversion from, the political, ethnic, and economic grievances from which the conflict largely derived. These centred on the longstanding but intensified discrimination by the Khartoum government against the

i Underlining the cynicism that many suspected lay behind the Russian veto in 2021 was the fact that it was Moscow that had been one of the capitals most supportive of the Government of Sudan throughout this period, and the keenest to prevent any sanctions being imposed on Khartoum for the systematic atrocities being committed. Indeed, the author, who at that time was working in the office of Secretary-General Ban, recalls being congratulated by a Russian diplomat for the *Washington Post* article. On the other hand, 14 years later, a top leader of one of the world's leading human rights organizations admitted to the present author, "we were wrong to criticise Ban Ki-moon for letting the Janjaweed off the hook in that article. The truth is that many in the human rights movement were slow to understand the enormity of climate change."

black communities of Darfur, as well as the brutal repression carried out by government-backed Janjaweed militias. Indeed, the 'climate war' rhetoric was adopted during a UN Security Council meeting by a delegate of then-President Omar al-Bashir as a way to absolve the government of its responsibilities.[48] Pinning the war in Darfur mainly on climate change would indeed have been misguided.[i] But denying that climate had any role in making the situation worse was equally so.[ii]

The arguments made by the Indian representative at the Security Council in 2021 likewise deserve attention. Suggestions that the Security Council is not the right place to discuss any matters beyond strict issues of international peace and security have always been made (usually to play down the obvious role of human rights violations in causing conflict and flows of refugees across borders, with China consistently at the forefront of this stance). Similarly, a number of governments without permanent seats feel that due to the excessive power and the undemocratic nature of the Security Council, especially the abuse of the veto by the permanent members, they need to push hard against any extension of its agenda into areas usually discussed in other UN bodies (such as human rights, development, and climate change). In addition, there has indeed been a lack of decisive action by governments under the UNFCCC, although whether including the issue of climate conflict on the Security Council's agenda would really have the effect of "obfuscating" the lack of action on climate mitigation issues, as suggested by the Government of India, is somewhat doubtful.[50]

For some, calling on the UN Security Council to act on climate change serves to 'securitise' the environmental issue in a dangerous

---

i As Ban Ki-moon was unfairly accused of doing, including by a curious alliance of human rights groups, climate sceptics and American neo-conservatives.

ii In his memoir published in 2021, the former Secretary-General returned to this issue, writing of Darfur, "It was understood to be a religious and ethnic conflict, but I believe the hostilities were based on competition for natural resources. Two decades of failed rains had led to hard droughts that turned much of Sudan into a dustbowl. Most of Sudan's remaining arable land was in Darfur." Two years later the *Economist* said Darfur had been dubbed the "first genocide" of the 21st century. "It may also have been the world's first climate change war. Reserve-rich but drought-prone, the region's land had long been contested as desertification spread and rainfall dwindled." The magazine added, importantly, "But it took the Arab- supremacist policies of Bashir and his Islamist allies to make Darfur explode."[49]

way that would lead to a mainly military outcome. As the old saying goes: "If all you have is a hammer, everything looks like a nail."[i] It is true that discussing climate change and security solely in this way would be undesirable, as it can lead to the perception that the *victims* of climate change and conflict are the *threat* that needs to be guarded against (for example when they become refugees looking for new, less infernal, places to live). This is why it would indeed be mistaken to see climate change solely as a 'security' issue. On the other hand, few people are suggesting that it should be. Others argue more persuasively that linking climate change with security (in all its forms, including human security, as well as development and human rights) in fact helps elevate the issue to more of an existential threat, bringing in a wider and more powerful coalition, thereby enabling and providing justification for governments to take the emergency actions (especially cuts to emissions) that are required to stave off planetary disaster.

The African Union's Peace and Security Council (AUPSC) has shown much less hesitancy in acknowledging the security implications of climate change. On the same day as the UN Security Council resolution was vetoed in 2021, the AUPSC issued a communiqué connecting climate, security and development as a core area of focus. Given its front-line position in the field of climate change and security, the AUPSC's commitment to linking these issues should be a lesson for other international bodies.

In contrast to the UN Security Council, the Western governments that constitute NATO have managed to reach agreement by at least recognising the security threat posed by climate change. Despite being originally set up to 'contain' what it saw as an aggressive Soviet Union, and given its new lease of life by the 2020 Russian full-scale invasion of Ukraine, NATO is now being forced to respond to this faceless – and even less predictable – threat. In its 2022 *Strategic Concept*, NATO not only unambiguously recognises the problem, declaring it to be "the defining challenge of our time", but aims to support civilian

i As put by the Indian delegate at the open debate held in the UN Security Council on 25 January 2019 (UNSC S/PV.8451).

crisis management and the use of military personnel in relief efforts in climate-induced disasters.[51]

Notwithstanding fears from some environmentalists that NATO muscling in on this subject represents an unwelcome 'securitised' hijacking of an agenda that should have no military component to it, it is surely a positive development if some of the enormous resources and political attention devoted to defence can be leveraged for climate purposes. It does not have to mean – as appears to be feared – that a blinkered, hatchet-faced military will now be inevitably focused on swinging their vast unsubtle hammer down on the human security nail.[i]

By and large, in comparison with other institutions in their respective societies, militaries tend to be well-resourced, large-scale and effective. They can be mobilised quickly and can provide support above and beyond their fighting capacities. The manpower that they provide has often been used in support of national interests that one would be stretched to call a 'militarisation', for example when they are deployed for humanitarian purposes following natural disasters or events such as the Covid-19 pandemic. In neither instance do the concerns over militarisation find a prominent place in the debate, and nor should they.

In this respect, there may well be the space for militaries to discuss climate change without driving the fears of militarisation, but it must be carefully defined. The tabling of climate migration as an item on the agenda of the Munich Security Conference (MSC) in February 2023 should be read in this way. In what could be seen as a departure from popular perceptions of what is normally talked about at the world's most high-level security

i One example of how the military mind-set does not need to lead to a 'securitised-only' approach can be found in the writings of former US General and Director of the CIA, David Petraeus.[52] He looked at how the 1815 eruption of Mount Tambora in Indonesia had an impact on weather patterns that may have helped decide the result of the Battle of Waterloo, as well as the cooling of the land in the Yangtze River Valley that contributed to the Qing dynasty's inability to manage famine-provoked unrest, and therefore China's 'century of humiliation'. This showed that the links between "climate change, national security, and the wellbeing of societies are undeniable and becoming increasingly pronounced". Petraeus and his fellow author cited the US Director of National Intelligence saying that the effects of climate change will fall overwhelmingly on the developing world, and concluded "climate change clearly exacerbates familiar pressures such as poverty, corruption, resource scarcity, and authoritarianism".

event, rather than discussing how the military can man the watchtowers and push back boats, it demonstrated an awareness of the human security implications of climate change among MSC participants.[i]

Issues of climate change and security are fraught with contention. This, alongside the high-level prevarication on the issue in global fora, can partly be attributed to the lack of consensus that still exists on what falls under the banner of 'climate security'. In July 2022, Annalena Baerbock, the German foreign minister and former leader of the Greens, declared climate change to be "the biggest security problem facing everyone on this earth". Her speech on climate and security covered topics ranging from the existential threat of sea-level rise to the people of Palau, to farmer-herder conflicts induced by climate change in Mali, and establishing energy security in the wake of Russia's invasion of Ukraine.[53] This breadth of topic illustrates the complexity of the issue.

In light of the confusion that surrounds the term climate security in policy communities, it should be noted that its evolution in academic circles has not been any smoother. The precise nature of the relationship between climate change and conflict (and security) has long been contested. Earlier studies on climate change and conflict, from the 1990s and beyond, took what was unexcitingly named a 'positivist quantitative approach', using large-scale surveys to identify a correlation between climate change and conflict. The benefit of this approach is that it makes it possible to test a hypothesis using a database consisting of thousands of observations; the number of observations lends credibility to the findings and therefore allows wider-reaching conclusions to be drawn. But it is not without its pitfalls.

To test the hypothesis that one partly causes the other, the first step is to set criteria for measuring each of the two variable elements, i.e. both climate change and conflict. This was the first point of disagreement among empirical researchers, who showed there was little consensus on how to do so, as a recent review revealed.[54] For instance, as a benchmark

---

i Sponsored by the Robert Bosch Foundation, the three panellists for the event were David Miliband, head of the humanitarian organisation the International Rescue Committee, Namira Negm, Director of the AU's African Migration Observatory in Morocco, and the author of this book.

of climate change, some have taken long- term changes over many decades (and indeed centuries),[55] while others have measured it by short-term climate variability, such as rainfall patterns,[56] natural disasters,[57] or drought frequency and intensity.[58]

Definitions of conflict have similarly varied, ranging from interpersonal conflict[59] and civil unrest[60], all the way to civil and international war.[61] This inconsistency has unsurprisingly made it hard to synthesise the findings, with some studies concluding that climate change (however defined) is a strong driver of violent conflict, and others (taking different definitions) proclaiming they have found no discernible effect.[62]

Academic disagreements like these do not happen in a vacuum – they are often caught up in personal predispositions and political motivations.[i] Much of the research in this area has been conducted by two prominent, although informal, research groups: one based in California, which has tended to find strong relationships between climate variables and conflict, and one based at the Peace Research Institute Oslo (PRIO).[64]

In 2009, the California-based scholar Marshall Burke and his colleagues published a much-cited article, "Warming increases the risk of civil war in Africa". Through their research they predicted that climate change would result in a 54 per cent increase in the risk of violent conflict outbreak by 2030, equating to an additional 393,000 battle deaths.[65] Based on their findings, they recommended urgent action by governments on the African continent.

i Some of the opposition to those who put forward the theory that climate change makes conflict worse seems to be verging on both the cynical (of the motives of others) and the ideological (in their own). Selby, for instance, has dismissed the positivist quantitavists' focus on Africa as a "popular Malthusian assumption, updated for the twenty-first century, that it is the poor who are the major cause of social disorder" emanating from "the global South – not from the liberal 'zone of peace'."63 He also claimed that the positivists' framing reflects "Northern complacency about the ways in which global climate change will challenge its forms of economy, politics and society, and a misplaced confidence that the worst effects of climate change will lie elsewhere". It is even implied that a motivation could be based on "military and aid industry interests in identifying new areas of intervention". So in short this type of research is "implicated in and shaped by a slew of political – and specifically Northern-led – narratives, interests and agendas".

But rather than responding to this alarming information and its call for action, several other researchers instead raised questions about the validity of these findings. In 2010, Halvard Buhaug from PRIO in Norway published a response, titled "Climate not to blame for African civil wars", to test the robustness of Burke et al.'s findings.[66] Among other changes, Buhaug reduced the criterion for measuring conflict from 1,000 to 25 annual battle-related deaths and included four common explanations of violent conflict to test the relative effect of climate factors.[i] In doing so, and despite using the same data sources as Burke et al., Buhaug estimated an almost negligible impact of climate change on conflict. According to his findings, climate change could explain only one per cent of the incidence of violent conflict.

It may be possible to read various motivations for scholars supporting the PRIO line. First, there were doubts about the methodological rigour of academics espousing the 'California' position, who (notwithstanding the alleged weaknesses of their arguments) rather annoyingly – at least in the eyes of the PRIO group – seemed to find it easier to achieve publicity and grants by making extravagant, 'cherry-picking' claims about the links, thereby skewing the debate. Secondly, if the causal claims were weak, then this could foster the position of climate change sceptics that all warnings about climate were exaggerated. Thirdly, there were understandable concerns that studies attributing conflict to environmental factors could be misused to downplay the significant political and governance causes of conflict. Lastly, as we have seen earlier in this chapter, there are some who fear that insisting on the linkages between climate change and conflict will – especially when the link goes through migration (see Chapter 4) – lead, wrongly, to hard securitised responses to climate change.

The debate between these two research groups continued for several years, with each new paper from one group leading to a response from the other criticising its method and message. Even if one regards the

---

i According to Buhaug, the first alteration was to respond more directly to "narratives of violent conflict within contexts of environmental marginalisation". The 'benchmark' explanations of civil war risk in Buhaug's models included: ethno-political exclusion, economic level of development, conflict history and the post-Cold War period.

figures presented by the 'California' group with a modicum of scepticism, it is hard not to find some cause for alarm in them. Given the lack of progress on emissions mitigation in the years since the paper was published, their models would presumably offer even more dire predictions had they been formulated in 2023. Despite the criticisms levelled at their paper, it is still cited in support of immediate climate action.

In his 2019 bestseller *The Uninhabitable Earth*, David Wallace-Wells paints a terrifying picture of what the planet will look like in the coming decades, with apocalyptic scenarios from heatwaves to economic collapse.[67] He argues that what was once alarmism has now become realism, and uses the findings of Burke et al. to make his case.[68] Some leading climate scientists – such as Michael Mann – have opposed this line, pointing out that the evidence of climate change's seriousness is overwhelming enough on its own, and thus "there is no need to overstate the evidence, particularly when it feeds a paralysing narrative of doom and hopelessness."[69] This is a vital point when dealing with any aspect of climate change, given the way in which some fossil fuel supporters make use of the doom- and-gloom exponents (who have the opposite view to the climate change sceptics but whose conclusions can in some instances point in a similar direction) to suggest that precisely because it is now too late to do anything, one might as well keep drilling and burning.[70]

Elsewhere, academic research on the relationship between climate change and conflict has struck a reasonable balance between the two schools, which has been described rather simplistically above, as getting too deeply into that old debate at this stage would seem of limited utility. Since the early assertions of each viewpoint (either too closely connecting the two phenomena, or else dismissing the interlinkages too brusquely), there has been growing recognition – particularly among the policy community – that climate change acts as a *risk multiplier*. In other words, climate change may not be the principal cause of a conflict, but nor does it lack all causal impact; rather, it adds both to the risk and the intensity of tensions, thereby increasing the likelihood of conflict and complicating the chances of finding a resolution.

The narrative of climate risk in armed conflict began in 2007 just as the wider issue of climate change was gaining traction in security circles in the US, as we have seen. Even 16 years later, this framing is still used amongst policymakers and practitioners. But what does it actually mean? According to Busby: *"it served the purpose of recognizing that there is a link between climate change and security without overstating its importance. By stating that climate is a 'threat multiplier', the speaker can assert that climate plays a role in making negative security outcomes more likely, but that it is not the sole driver and that its influence happens in concert with other factors."*[71]

In this sense, the multiplier framing is a useful one: it allows one to avoid committing to too bald a position (such as 'climate change causes conflict'). Instead, it creates space for the more nuanced claim that climate change makes known conflict drivers even more complicated. Even for those who play down any linkage, it is hard to dismiss that logic. Nevertheless, there is still a need to identify exactly what those risks are – knowledge that is essential to any kind of targeted response.

On this front, academic research has complemented progress made in the policy community. In 2019, a group of the most prominent experts from both sides of the debate were consulted for an 'expert elicitation' – a method sometimes used for a review of evidence on contentious topics. Between them, they concluded that climate change would exacerbate existing drivers of conflict, such as low socioeconomic development, low state capabilities, intergroup inequality, and a recent history of violent conflict.[72] Their findings suggest, for example, that climate shocks will be less likely to induce conflict in areas with a more peaceful recent history and high intergroup equality than in areas beset by intractable conflicts and social marginalisation.

Amidst this somewhat innocuous language lies a sinister truth. We know that conflict undermines socioeconomic development and state capabilities while also – in many cases – deepening economic inequalities. But if the areas where climate change makes conflict that much worse are also those that are unfortunate enough to be *already* in conflict, then the possibility of creating a 'conflict trap' arises.

Across much of Somalia and Sudan, inequality, poverty, a history of conflict and a weak state are all evident. Combine these with a high exposure to climate change, and a cycle could soon emerge, with conflict creating vulnerability to climate change, which in turn drives additional conflict, leading to even greater vulnerability, and yet more conflict and so on. To characterise climate change here as a multiplier of risk would be to underplay its influence. In this instance, climate change acts not only as a risk multiplier, but also as a peace inhibitor.[73]

Our current climate trajectory means that special attention should be paid to these areas. Most studies performed to establish the relationship between climate and conflict deal with the past history of warming. By definition, therefore, they only treat the 1.1°C of mean global temperature increase that has been seen so far. According to the Climate Action Tracker, policies currently in place will in future produce warming of 2.6-2.9°C,[74] while many other estimates present an even bleaker picture. However one assesses the current ambitions of limiting this to 1.5°C, or even to 2°C, the planet will continue to warm in the years to come and enter territory characterised by unpredictability and extremes.

While this should in no way be interpreted to mean that the need for mitigation measures is questioned,[i] it does indicate that adaptation strategies need to be prepared and massively accelerated. This is necessary to handle not only the relatively limited dislocation already experienced, but also the far greater ones that seem almost certain in the future. Since the greatest dislocations of all seem destined to fall on conflict-prone areas, it is these areas that policymakers should pay particular attention to, not least as the conflicts will probably intensify, adding new layers of risk to existing security concerns.

Often implicit in modelling of the correlation between climatic variations and conflict is the assumption that a further increase of 1°C will have proportionately the same effect as the previous 1°C increase. This assumption seems to downplay the likelihood of tipping points

---

i As is now being pushed by former climate change sceptics of the Koch and Murdoch ilk, who have adjusted their arguments to suggest that since it is inevitable, there is no point spending resources to move away from fossil fuels.[75]

and assumes that effects will increase more or less linearly. In addition, we have already seen that a global average of 1°C can translate to much higher temperatures and more extreme weather events in specific areas. The question of whether climate change has *so far* contributed much to conflict may have been hotly debated, but it is of limited value to practitioners who need to assess how intensified climate change could cause conflict *in the future*, and how such conflict can be averted.[i] It is therefore important to move beyond the empirical analyses of past climatic variability towards projections of climate change impacts. This will allow for a more joined up approach between the academic and practitioner spheres,[77] and will better enable the formation of an effective (and inter-disciplinary) agenda to prevent the destabilising effect of climate change on peace.

Whether it is geopolitical competition over a thawing Arctic, the growth of violent extremism partly as a result of drought in Somalia, drying rivers impeding trade in Western Europe and hydro-electric power generation in China, or more frequent hurricanes in the eastern United States: all these issues can legitimately be viewed as interconnected matters of climate and security. In both practitioner and policy circles, there is little shared assessment of how these risks should be addressed, and their breadth and variation mean that different bodies will be better suited to address different aspects.[78] Suggestions on practical ways to address the risks posed by climate change – especially in a peacebuilding context – remain exceedingly limited. It would help if there were a common understanding that climate change should be seen as a risk to broader human security. This would involve policy-makers recognising that the real threat is posed mainly to communities, especially the least prosperous among them, rather than to nation states as a whole (with the obvious exception of small island states, for whose populations rising sea levels represent an almost apocalyptic threat), and therefore that social and economic development and well-chosen adaptation measures should be the utmost priority.

---

i The focus has long been on causality, which, as a recent UNDP report reasonably puts it, has created a body of literature that "does not yield operationally relevant recommendations for tackling climate-related security risks."[76]

The imperative of finding practical solutions will need to be centred first on conflict-sensitive adaptation measures. This means devising a preventive response to climate and security risks by reducing social and environmental vulnerabilities, and doing so in a way that does not contribute to tensions that underlie existing conflicts or could help provoke new ones. As part of this response, a second (and related) area worth exploring lies in environmental peacebuilding. This would involve trying to encourage parties in a given conflict to see their environmental problems (whether deriving from climate change or other causes) not just as an additional factor driving conflict, although they often are that, but as a potential basis of common ground that could foster peace.

These issues will be analysed in subsequent chapters. But first we need to look at how people have tried to identify climate risk.

3 What do we know about the risks?

The struggle for control of vital natural resources such as land and water is as old as humanity itself. The conflicts they have inspired have ranged from those between states, where militaries have intervened to secure key water sources, to small-scale fighting between communities where farmers and herders clash over access to pasture. This seems unlikely to change. But what distinguishes the current era, and even more the decades to come, from whatever has been seen previously is the intensification and increased frequency of clashes due to climate change.

Climate change exacerbates existing tensions and renders resolutions increasingly challenging. The intricate web of causation between climate change and violent conflicts makes drawing a clear line between the two overly simplistic, as seen previously. The present chapter therefore attempts to unfurl some of this complexity by looking at how human decision-making — and therein bad governance, social inequality, and violence — can create further reasons for conflict to emerge and escalate. Looking at how human decisions impact our vulnerability to natural phenomena is useful; it focuses on factors that are in our power to change, rather than on things beyond our control. This approach is not new, however.

In 1755, one of the first 'modern disasters' struck the city of Lisbon. An earthquake – estimated at a magnitude of 9 on the Richter scale – shook the city centre, destroying countless buildings. It was soon followed by a tsunami, inundating many of the low-lying areas while fire tore through the wooden buildings that were still standing. The catastrophe claimed thousands of lives.[79] Confronted by the scale of destruction wrought apparently by nature (though not of course climate change), Voltaire's faith in an all-powerful and benevolent creator was rocked. The crisis created by the earthquake was to him a natural phenomenon, in which humankind was the hapless victim. But for his contemporary, Jean- Jacques Rousseau, Voltaire had got the nature of this crisis all wrong.

Responding in 1756, Rousseau questioned whether calling the earthquake a natural disaster was a misnomer. He contended that there was nothing actually natural to it, since "it was hardly nature who assembled there 20,000 houses of six or seven stories." If the residents of that large city had been "more evenly dispersed and less densely housed, the losses would have been fewer or perhaps none at all".[80] The 'disaster', in this sense, was therefore socially created;[i] sure, the geological event itself was indeed entirely natural, but what caused it to turn it into a full-blown disaster were misguided human decisions.

Faced with modern academic disagreements around climate change and conflict, this analogy from one of the early forays into what has later been termed 'disaster science' provides a useful framing for the discourse on climate and security, particularly for peace practitioners. Conflicts, even more than Rousseau's disasters, are a product of human processes and decisions. By itself, a severe drought is not a reason to engage in violence, and nor is a flood. But the ways in which such phenomena may affect diverse aspects of the social and political realm can indeed contribute to conflict. The environmental event is not the sole determinant of insecurity, but rather it changes the conditions in which human societies make decisions. In the right conditions, these

i Rousseau's analysis of this event places the natural phenomena within a human social and cultural context, and so marks an early example of a social science perspective, as argued by Dynes.[81]

kinds of shocks can prompt cooperation rather than conflict. By maintaining the focus on social (as opposed to natural) aspects of risk, it may also help to avoid slipping into the climate fatalism alluded to in the previous chapter, which can make environmental action appear pointless. And by correctly identifying the social phenomena that cause climate vulnerability beyond the worsening climate itself, new avenues may open for action on climate and security.

Recent research has begun to factor in this perspective. Instead of trying to plot – or alternatively deny the existence of – a direct line between climate change and conflict, some studies have looked to identify the chain of causes and effects that may connect the two. By analysing this question of *how* climate change affects conflict, it becomes possible to identify the social processes that link the two, as well as possible entry points to prevent conflict from breaking out.

A much more recent example of the factors debated in mid-18th century Lisbon was on display in September 2023 in Libya. 'Storm Daniel' hammered the country's eastern coastal region with wind and rain, leading to the collapse of two dams constructed above the city of Derna, which caused thousands of residents to be washed out to sea. As one climate scientist explained, warmer water "not only fuels those storms in terms of rainfall intensity, it also makes them more ferocious," making what happened "likely a result of warmer sea surface and hence man-made climate change as well."[82] Yet human error, conflict, and corruption also played a major role in the tragedy. Libya has been in a state of civil war since 2011 following the NATO intervention and the killing of President Gaddafi. Derna and the region in which it is located has long been occupied by a warlord fighting against the UN-backed government, Khalid Haftar, who has received much foreign support, including from France, Egypt, the UAE, and the Russian-based Wagner Group. Despite receiving sizeable sums to repair the dams which experts had long warned about, the authorities in Derna appear to have simply pocketed the funds without bothering to repair the dams. Thus, one can conclude that climate change by itself did not cause the tragedy; and nor did corruption. The high loss of lives, as so often in history, derived from the combination of natural and human causes, in this instance fuelled by climate change.[83]

What follows in this chapter is an attempt to synthesise the relevant research and to explore how climate risks can become intertwined with issues of peace and security. It focuses on the physical and material challenges created by climate change, and how these can be exacerbated by human decisions, designs, and behaviour.

Other than extreme heat, the most immediate impact of climate change is the depletion – because of new weather patterns – of various categories of natural resources. Countries where most livelihoods depend directly on these resources, often through relatively underdeveloped agriculture, stand to suffer the most. As we saw with particular virulence on every continent in 2022, climate change is already resulting in an increase in the frequency and intensity of extreme weather events, such as droughts, extreme heat, floods, and storms. These events damage the production of crops and diminish essential clean water sources. In areas where the quality and availability of resources such as water and fertile soil determine livelihood opportunities, climate change undermines human security and fosters the socioeconomic conditions known (with certainty) to drive violent conflict.

This is being experienced in Somalia, which is especially susceptible to the impacts of climate change (it is second only to Niger as the most vulnerable country worldwide).[84] In 2022, newly elected President Hassan Sheikh Mohamud developed a six-pillar Government Programme that included addressing the effects of climate change, land degradation, natural disasters, and desertification. This programme was to be undertaken as a priority, he pointed out, as analysts projected an increase in the duration of droughts, as well as more erratic rainfall, disruption to the monsoon seasons, and more natural disasters.[85] These climatic conditions would be challenging anywhere, but pose particular difficulties for Somalia, where agriculture and livestock husbandry account for about 72 per cent of the country's employment. It is not hard to discern how climate shocks may increase the risk of conflict.[86] Severe droughts prompt livestock owners to sell off some of their herds, since there is less available water and pasture to sustain them. As more animals come onto the market, prices are driven down, reducing herders' ability to maintain a living and resulting in displacement on a vast scale and rapid urbanisation, with which the country cannot keep pace. At this point, the prospect of joining an armed group (the largest of which in Somalia are Islamist and advocates of extreme violence) may become a necessity or at least more attractive than persistently toiling under desperate conditions.

Similarly in India, agricultural yields have been diminished by an increasing number of climate shocks, made worse by the Green Revolution farming practices that have compacted and destroyed the country's soil. Many farmers' harvests have been ruined, leaving them with few remaining livelihood opportunities. At times, lingering discontent has grown, accompanied by outbreaks of political and religious violence. In 2020 and 2021, the country faced some of the largest protests in its history when the government tried to push through three agricultural reform acts, threatening to undermine the minimum support price for crops, which had guaranteed a livelihood to many farmers struggling under increasingly challenging conditions. The protests lasted over a year and led to the deaths of around 750 farmers.[87] Recent research conducted not only finds a robust relationship between changing weather patterns and political violence,[i] but also suggests that areas that have suffered from chronic conflict in the past – notably Jammu and Kashmir, but also Tripura, Assam, Nagaland, and Manipur in the northeast – will be most vulnerable to its recurrence.[88]

As climate change erodes natural resources, it can alter the strategic value of key resources This opens new avenues of influence for armed groups.[89] When the productivity of land decreases due to climatic changes or extreme weather events, or when resources are depleted by drought, land and water increase in strategic value. Possession of these resources not only creates opportunities for new forms of revenue-raising by armed groups but may also enable them to dispense largesse, patronage and social services. This builds up political support

i Scientists draw a distinction between *climate change* (which refers to long-term variations, usually now connected to human activities) and *climate variability* (shorter-term changes attributable to natural causes, a well-known example of which is El Niño. For the purposes of this book, the distinction does not appear especially useful, not least as many of the regions of the world most vulnerable to conflict are those that are also subject to higher-than-global-average effects of climate change.

for these armed groups and may even enhance their legitimacy among the local population.

The war against ISIS (or 'Islamic State') in Iraq and Syria came after years of recurring droughts. When ISIS emerged in 2013 and sought to take control of first Iraq and then Syria, they saw water as a strategic resource. At the peak of their territorial control in 2015, they had captured three of Syria's most important dams – the Tishrin, Tabqa, and Baath Dams – and controlled several strategic water sources in their Iraqi territory.

This allowed them to pocket the revenues from hydroelectric power and also gave them another weapon. After capturing the Ramadi Dam in Iraq in 2015, they began diverting water into Lake Habbaniya to reduce the flow of water in the Euphrates by almost 50 per cent, thereby depriving the downstream Anbar province of a water supply. Only a year before, they had used the dams at Falluja, Samarra, and Mosul to prevent much needed water from reaching Shiite areas.[90]

Halting the flow was not the only part of their water strategy. Closing the Falluja Dam sluice gates, they flooded areas upstream where Iraqi government facilities were located. Elsewhere, they poisoned drinking water with crude oil and poured rubble into wells. According to Amnesty International, ISIS's actions and the effects on rural communities and their water supplies showed evidence of war crimes and crimes against humanity. Once defeat had been declared over ISIS in 2017, one (now former) farmer reflected on what this environmental destruction meant as he returned home: "I had a well – 220 metres deep – as well as a generator and an irrigation pipe system. They threw rubble in my well and filled it to the top. My trees were chopped down ... The irrigation system – from the pump to the pipes – was stolen. They did this to send a message: that you have nothing to return to, so if you survive don't even think of coming back."[91]

The environmental impacts of war can make post-conflict reconstruction difficult anywhere, but when parties to a conflict actively target such essential elements of survival, recovery may become impossible, especially when the effects of conflict are made so much worse thanks to climate change.

Controlling the flow of water gave ISIS leverage over a resource which assumed even more strategic importance after years of intense drought. They were able to curry favour with potential allies and to place extreme – in some cases life- threatening – pressure on hostile groups, thereby increasing influence for their ideological ends. And while they may be the most well-known example of an armed group profiting from the impacts of climate change, they are far from unique. Climate change has already opened new opportunities for recruitment by Boko Haram in the Lake Chad Basin and by al-Shabaab in Somalia.

A few decades ago, Lake Chad supported the livelihoods of many communities living in the Sahel and was a trading hub for the region. Droughts in the 1970s and 1980s saw the lake's surface area decline by over 90 per cent over 40 years. This contraction inevitably made making a living far more difficult for the communities dependent on the lake. Weak governance and social service provision worsened their relationship with the state, and groups with extremist ideologies began to proliferate throughout the Basin. Since 2002, the most prominent has been Boko Haram, whose rise came off the back of protests against economic inequality and corruption. They have targeted disenfranchised youth to join their ranks, promising them a better life.

Since reaching its lowest point of 2,000 km^2 in the 1980s, down from 25,000 km^2 two decades earlier, the water level in Lake Chad has since risen again and stabilised at around 14,000 km^2.[i] [93] But the lake is still not the hub of economic opportunity that it once was, with this manifestation of climate change now impacting some of the root causes of conflict in the area. Weather patterns are becoming increasingly unpredictable, fostering additional insecurity among those dependent

i The dramatic reduction in water surface area during the 1980s was due to prolonged and severe droughts – a phenomenon often pointed to as the early indications of climate change. This may have been true insofar as it described the droughts, but not when it was used to explain the shrinkage of the lake. Since then, the increase in rainfall in the tropical areas from where the lake's tributaries run has led to an increase in groundwater levels and subsequently ensured relative stability in the level of the lake.[92]

on agriculture. As farming becomes a less reliable source of income throughout the region, the economic inequalities and marginalisation of some communities that catalysed the rise of Boko Haram in the first place have become even more pronounced – a narrative which the group has successfully capitalised on to try to legitimise its standing with the population.

The responses of regional governments to the rise of armed groups in the Lake Chad Basin have also worsened the risk posed by climate change. Rather than shoring up communities' resilience to the changing climate conditions, the militarised and often brutal responses by security forces have cut communities off from access to land and so reduced their opportunities for economic activity.[94] The social contract – fragile at the best of times in these states – has been further undermined by major human rights violations carried out by government security forces and allied militia groups.

In the six years from 2009 to 2015, it is estimated that over 20,000 civilians were killed by Boko Haram.[95] Refusal to join them, to accept their beliefs, or even failure to recite the Quran has led to torture and execution. Thousands have also been abducted; women have been forcibly separated from their 'unbelieving' husbands and subjected to sexual abuse, harassment and the deprivation of fundamental rights such as food and water. The government-led counter-insurgency efforts have not always been better. In areas of Cameroon, Niger, and Nigeria, young men are facing the double threat of abduction and torture by Boko Haram, and arrest and detention by government forces as Boko Haram suspects. Nigerian civilians in arbitrary detention have also been deprived of food and water; these conditions have led to an average of five deaths a day amongst detainees.[96] Given the deep disaffection this causes towards the Nigerian state in these areas, it is becoming increasingly unlikely that the affected communities will want to cooperate with the government in any large-scale adaptation strategies.

The role of climate change in the Lake Chad Basin amply demonstrates the risk multiplier effect. Drawing a straight line between climate change and conflict, as we have seen, might be misleading.

But by adding stress to vulnerable livelihoods and driving economic marginalisation in areas that were already among the poorest in the world, climate change has deepened divides between groups and areas, and made adapting to the new climate reality even more difficult.

Looking only at how climate change can multiply risks may leave us feeling somewhat helpless. But, as with Rousseau's earthquake, human decisions can contribute much to the disasters; or rather, it is the conditions in society that either do or do not translate the natural risk into a natural disaster. In the case of Lake Chad, both the regional wealth gaps and government human rights abuses mean that the harmful effects of climate change are even more devastating, driving food shortages and human insecurity. In regions in the Sahel and elsewhere, it is the lack of effective governance that has exposed people to such climate-related security risks, as recognised in the most recent IPCC Assessment Report.[97] Focusing on these human decisions and the state of governance in conflict areas can therefore provide another useful framing of climate-related conflict risk, and one that opens meaningful entry points to address it.

At the border between Iran and Afghanistan, the Helmand River feeds into Hamun Lake, after snaking 1,000 km from Afghanistan's Hindu Kush. The river has long been a vital source of water for Iran's eastern provinces of Sistan and Baluchistan, where political and economic marginalisation has driven protests in recent years. The two countries have for centuries disputed the sharing of water from the Helmand River. In a treaty signed in 1973, it was agreed that Iran would receive 850 million cubic metres per year. However, the failure to implement this commitment, exacerbated by political instability, has seen the dispute escalate.

In May 2023, clashes briefly broke out along the border killing three people. Both sides accused the other of opening fire. This escalation has not come out of nowhere. In 2021, a year when an estimated 97 per cent of Iran was impacted by drought, the Afghan government opened the Kamal Khan Dam. At its inauguration, President Ashraf Ghani declared Afghanistan would "no longer give free water to anyone, so Iran should provide fuel to Afghans in exchange for water,"[98] all the while insisting that the dam did not break the 1973 treaty. In the following two years, droughts in the region (made more likely by climate change) have resulted in even less water reaching the dam, and even less arriving in Iran – estimated at four per cent of the designated share under the 1973 treaty, as claimed by one Iranian official.[99] Climate conditions are making an equitable agreement more challenging, but the decisions taken principally by the current Taliban regime will be the factor that determines whether this conflict will escalate. If the Iranian government and the Taliban can work towards a diplomatic solution (as they both claim is their intent), the growing climate pressures may be alleviated. Trying to solve it by force or unilateral action will almost certainly lead to further escalation.

The Middle East and North Africa Region contains 12 of the 17 most water scarce countries in the world; its vulnerability to water scarcity is well known. The network of rivers that traverse borders provides an opportunity for regional cooperation and mutual benefit, but when this fails, countries downstream pay the biggest price. In Iraq, where the main flow of water comes from the Tigris and Euphrates rivers, supply has decreased by 30 per cent since 1980.[100] Neighbouring Turkey has dammed both rivers, while Iran has reduced the supply to one of the major Tigris tributaries.[101] But this is only part of the problem. Climate change, heavy industrial usage, government policy, and weak law enforcement have all further compounded water scarcity in Iraq.

Between Iraq's provinces, quotas have been put in place by the central government to ensure that the supplies are divided equitably, and to avoid over-extraction. Nonetheless, the agreements of the volumes of water to be distributed have been flouted. Disputes on over-consumption have arisen between provinces, with limited responses from the government. In the absence of specific and effective resolution mechanisms, there is an increased risk of these disputes escalating into violence.[102]

The problem comes not only from domestic actors; foreign oil companies have also exploited the lack of environmental regulation in Iraq. In Basra governorate, access to potable water is extremely limited: 80 per cent of the population have access to water for less than 10 hours per day.[103] And even when they do, it is of poor quality; in 2018, 118,000 people were taken to hospital due to water-related diseases, prompting demonstrations against the government that resulted in the death of five protestors.[104]

Corruption similarly compounds the conflict risks of climate change. In the Iraqi province of Kirkuk (a political hotspot in the country, with Iraq's three main ethnic groups – Arab, Kurdish, and Turkmen – all laying strong and mutually exclusive historical claims at the others' expense, in part owing to the presence of large oil reserves there), a total of 41 fishing ponds have been legally permitted. These ponds require a significant volume of water, and so, given the pressing issue of water scarcity in Iraq, their number has been limited. Nonetheless, over 400 of these ponds now exist in Kirkuk, a number too high to have escaped the notice of local authorities, suggesting complicity in their construction.[105] Corruption has contributed to more and more water being drawn from public sources, reinforcing water scarcity and further fuelling inter-provincial (and therefore inter-ethnic, especially Arab-Kurdish) tensions.

As explored in a recent Berghof report,[106] conflict in Yemen has produced a similarly vicious cycle around water scarcity – one of the foremost challenges facing the country. The origins of this environmental disaster go back many years, however. In the early 1970s, the oil boom started in earnest in Saudi Arabia. This new industry needed vast new labour resources, promising stable wages in a growing economy. Two to three million Yemenis heard this call and migrated to neighbouring Saudi Arabia to earn a living. But their departure did not spell wealth for the families and villages left behind. Without sufficient manpower needed to maintain the farming terraces, the women and children who remained at home resorted to cutting down trees as fuel for cooking and heating. With the trees gone and the farming terraces slowly disintegrating, the water coming down in Yemen's once reliable rainfall cycles runs off the hillsides, taking with it much of the fertile soil, and silting the *wadis* (seasonal riverbeds). The wadis could no longer support the two or three crops a year that they could previously. Many turned instead to growing *qat* – a water-hungry cash crop – leading to over-extraction of groundwater.[107]

Now, eight years after the most recent conflict began in Yemen, the environmental conditions are even worse. The degradation that started in the 1970s continues, while climate change drives the country still deeper into crisis. More intense droughts and irregular downpours have made farming difficult. Rains come in the form of heavy storms, washing away even more of the remaining topsoil that sustains agriculture. Cyclones arrive in greater number, destroying wells for drinking water and washing away land boundaries.

These conditions would be challenging anywhere, but in Yemen, where the effects of climate change and lack of rainfall have long posed a problem, intractable conflict and weak governance are making its population even more vulnerable. Fuel shortages created by the war have led to communities abandoning their diesel-powered water pumps. Instead, many have turned to more efficient and cheaper solar-powered equivalents, which (rather paradoxically for such an environmentally friendly source of energy) have had a far from benign effect on local ecology. Rather than increasing the water supply, the ability to extract more water faster has led to historically low levels in the aquifers. According to a former minister for the environment and water: "In Sana, the capital, in the 1980s, you had to drill about 60 meters to find water. Today, you have to drill 850 to 1,000 meters to find water. Yemen has 15 aquifers, and only two today are self-sustaining; all the others are being steadily depleted." [108]

In 2010, before the current war started, 4,000 people were killed in land and water disputes each year according to one estimate from the Government of Yemen.[109] Competition over water is fierce and continues to spark local conflicts between farmers. Water scarcity in Yemen is caused not only by over-consumption, but also by the absence of oversight and enforcement of environmental standards. The conflict has created a population of internally displaced persons (IDP) in Yemen of around 4.5 million.[110] Often migrating towards urban areas, they place an additional burden on infrastructure and institutions. In need of housing, many have taken to constructing buildings right next to riverbeds where flood risks are high in the wake of storms. In May 2021, more than 1,000 houses were damaged in this way along the Wadi Hadramawt.[111] The poor management of this IDP influx and a lack of regulation have caused the riverbanks to deteriorate, reducing the amount of fertile land available for agriculture. Meanwhile, wells are being destroyed, and others polluted by animal corpses and excrement dumped upstream.[112]

Across wide areas, especially in Africa, weak institutions and poor natural resource management have also aggravated tensions between pastoralists and farmers – a relationship already strained by years of conflict and poverty. From the 1970s to the 1990s, recurrent droughts hit parts of Darfur, driving pastoralists and sedentary farmers alike to seek livelihoods in more rain-abundant areas. Arab camel herders from the north of Darfur looked for alternative transhumance routes in the south, where the droughts had not been so severe. But by moving, they begun to encroach on land owned by non-Arab groups such as the Masalit and the Fur. After the Sudanese government's decision in 1970 to strip traditional tribe-based institutions of their rights to land management and allocation, there were fewer avenues to resolve conflicts emerging over natural resource scarcity. In the absence of these (even informal) institutions, the increasing number of people and the diversity of groups put a heavy strain on communities' usual ways of resolving disputes. There were more people, needing additional resources, but with a different way of doing things.

Areas that received higher rainfall naturally attracted more people, prompting violent clashes in several places, especially in southern Darfur,[113] which culminated in the first genocide of the 21st century, starting in 2003. The combination of weak institutions exacerbated by poor governance, exceptional brutality, and natural resource scarcity undermined the capacity for peaceful conflict resolution in Darfur.

But it is not only around water that these issues arise, as the case of the acacia trees in Somalia shows. The lack of enforcement of the ban on charcoal production since 1969 has led to the decimation of the acacia tree population. Weak rule of law paired with vague rules on resource ownership has allowed millions of trees to be cut down for charcoal production (2.1 million per year, according to one estimate).[114] While this has provided a source of short-term income for some people (as well as an important revenue stream for al-Shabaab), its real impact is much more long-lasting. This deforestation increases an area's vulnerability to severe flooding, since the trees are no longer there to store water and maintain soil integrity. And even worse, when these trees are burned, they destroy the biodiversity in the surrounding area, leaving the soil irreparably damaged. The livelihoods of pastoralists who depend on feeding acacia leaves to their animals are therefore jeopardised – and the experience from many other parts of Africa (including Mali, Burkina Faso, the Lake Chad Basin, and Sudan) shows how much potential there is for conflict when pastoralists find themselves in such a situation.

The knock-on effects of the acacia demise are already being felt in Somalia. The nomadic, pastoralist way of life is no longer feasible for much of the country. Deforestation has left communities with no trees to feed their goats and camels. More herders are either losing their livestock and livelihoods, or coming into conflict with the farmers because their animals eat their crops. One long-term strategy would be for the herders to stay put – not roam the land with their livestock– and receive fodder instead of grazing. If the choice is between losing all their livestock to drought and starvation, or becoming more stationary with fewer animals in a more enclosed, ranch-style arrangement, pragmatism would dictate the latter. But the understandable attachment to a traditional, nomadic way of life has made this transition much more difficult.[i]

An important social and political dimension that should be recognised as part of the climate-conflict discussion is gender. It is well established that climate change impacts different groups in different ways. In almost every context mentioned so far, women are facing increased workloads and growing health risks, as well as higher rates of gender-based violence – partly because of climate change.

---

i As found in research conducted in 2022 by the Berghof Foundation Somalia Team as part of the project "Infrastructures for Peace and Inclusive Dialogue in Galmudug State".

Many parts of Africa, north and south of the Sahara, are already experiencing temperatures well above 30° C, making daily tasks such as collecting firewood and water even more challenging for women's health and wellbeing.[115] Their journeys are becoming more perilous as the decline in water and firewood sources requires women to travel further, and increasingly exposes them to the risk of violence.

Population displacement that is caused by climate change similarly places an unequal burden on women. Between 2005 and 2018, the rate of internal displacement tripled in Somalia. Two extreme droughts in 2011 and 2017, alongside growing violence across the country, saw 2.6 million people displaced, driving many to settle in IDP camps.[116] In such camps, little protection is afforded by the poorly constructed shelters, and the customary clan-based protection mechanisms against harassment are disrupted, increasing the risk of sexual violence. Women in the camps from a minority clan or marginalised group are particularly at risk.[117] The current drought, which began in 2021 and is considered the worst in 40 years, has already displaced one million Somalis, according to UNHCR figures.[118] The rate of sexual violence against women who find shelter in these camps will likely exceed those seen after the droughts of 2011 and 2017.

In Chad, women have long been excluded from accessing and controlling natural resources. Instances of child, early and forced marriage are not uncommon, and the rights of children and women clash with customary laws.[119] Particularly around Lake Chad, climate change makes agricultural livelihoods more difficult to maintain, and women are finding themselves in a cycle of everyday violence. Disregarding women's abilities to manage these resources places a considerable financial burden on the rest of the household; when land degradation and soil erosion reduce the opportunities to relieve this financial burden, households are less likely to pay for girls' education, making them more vulnerable to early marriage; at the same time, the young men become more susceptible to armed groups' blandishments.[120] In their interaction with climate change, politically-embedded discrimination and violence create a downward spiral of insecurity.

It is not only on the domestic or state level that weak governance results in climate-related security issues. It is also the international community's failure to take this dynamic fully into account that can render support ineffective, and even harmful, as has been the case in Mali.

As we have seen, a long-term decrease in rainfall and recurrent drought – a trend now made worse by climate change[i] – has placed an additional strain on relations between semi-nomadic herders and sedentary farmers. But when the rains do come, competition over this much-awaited abundance can likewise lead to violence, mirroring a situation described by Kenyan herdsmen: "raiders like to attack during wet years because of high grass, strong animals, dense bush to hide in and the availability of surface water, which makes it easier to trek with the animals."[121] Some herders will endure and cooperate during a dry period, waiting for the rains to come to steal from their enemies and replenish their lost livestock. After a prolonged period of scarcity, the arrival of an abundance of a resource can increase risk of conflicts, most acutely in areas where institutions to manage them (government or otherwise) are inadequate.

Climate change is only one of several drivers of insecurity in Mali, as it is elsewhere.[ii] After Mali gained its independence in 1960, the government implemented various land reform policies to boost the country's agricultural productivity. But to achieve this, they favoured sedentary communities, privileging them with land rights and titles. Naturally, this upset herder communities whose livelihoods required access to the pastureland that were now formally held by sedentary farmers – and these tensions were exacerbated by the increasing use of

---

i There were additional anthropogenic factors in the region's ecological degradation beyond the greenhouse gas emissions that have caused climate change. As in many countries of the Sahel, the large increase in the human population led to the cutting down of vast quantities of vegetation for firewood, and the increase in livestock numbers resulted in overgrazing and the erosion of topsoil, making it even harder to grow crops.

ii This part of the world has, historically, been no stranger to devastating climate change with an impact on conflict. In the 1590s, increasing desertification is thought to have played a role in the weakening of the Songhai Empire, which led to its collapse and the capture of Timbuktu by Moroccan forces. Timbuktu never recovered the position it had held, with climate migration causing the population of the region to shrink.[122]

land for rice cultivation, which displaced many of the wild plants and grasses that herders relied on for livestock fodder, and also used up large quantities of water.

The disputes that arise between farmers and herders tend to follow ethnic lines, and have occurred more and more frequently in recent years. It is estimated that there are over 20 million Fulani (or Peulh) spread across several countries in West Africa and the Sahel, many of whom see themselves as a nation without their own state. A sizeable proportion of them are herdsmen living in the northern, drier parts of countries whose armies, as with Mali and Niger, tend to be drawn from the sedentary farmers and ethnic groups that live in more savannah-type lands of the south. The discrimination they feel has led to some being recruited into extremist groups which benefit from the combination of climate-induced droughts and human rights abuses – with both sets of hardships, the Fulani feel, being disproportionately experienced by their group.

In one incident in Mali in March 2019, for example, more than 150 Fulani herders were killed by a militia formed by Dogon farmers, while a Fulani attack on Dogon villages killed 35 people in June the same year. Feuds based on ethnic identities provide not only the means to contest resource access, but have been instrumentalised by jihadist groups, such as Jama'at Nusrat al-Islam wal Muslimeen (JNIM). Aligning themselves with some in the Fulani community, they have exploited the grievances created by the land tenure system that privileges Dogon and Bambara farmers at the expense of Fulani herders.[123] Now, as each of these attacks prompts acts of retaliation, a cycle of violence is developing between the groups and with no recourse to legal solutions.

Understanding the complex dynamics in Mali is crucial for any effective response, and focusing on one of these dynamics can lead to other conflict-driving factors being exacerbated. Natural resources have been an important part the EU's investment in agricultural development in Mali. As part of its support for the Sahel Alliance, the EU contributes almost 5 billion euros to agricultural development across the five countries.[124] On top of this substantial development assistance, the EU currently has two missions working in Mali: the EUTM aims to provide support for the Malian armed forces; while EUCAP provides capacity-building for police and internal security forces. Both missions' ultimate aim is counter-terrorism.

International efforts to combat terrorism in Mali (and elsewhere) are sometimes less productive than they could be.[125] In these efforts external actors have, when government forces are absent, often found it easier to accommodate ethnically-based militias, who work in broad alliance with the government under the banner of counter-terrorism. Such is the case in Mali. But as can be seen from the conflict between the Dogon and Fulani militias, working with these groups has its own negative ramifications for peace efforts.[i]

As these militias clash violently with their rivals, and resource conflicts continue to break out, counter-terrorism efforts are undermined. The brutal practices frequently used by government-backed militias have increased recruitment into the very armed groups that the counter-terrorist strategy was meant to combat in the first place.[126] Although this appears to be slowly changing, the roles of climate change and human right violations have not been sufficiently considered in counter-terrorism strategies.

Similar patterns can be observed in other countries of the Sahel – especially Burkina Faso, Chad, Mauritania, and Niger – and important steps have been taken to reverse this trend. Recognising the changing security landscape in this region, a joint AU-ECOWAS-UN assessment has been commissioned, to be led by former Nigerien

---

i In other instances, however, EU support has enabled innovative approaches to counter-terrorism. For example, funding has been granted to the United Nations Office of the High Commissioner for Human Rights to develop and support implementation of the 'compliance framework approach' (with the Joint Force of the G5-Sahel as well as with the African Union for its peace support operations). This approach seeks to build awareness that compliance with international standards during military operations is not only a moral imperative but an operational necessity; it enhances security and decreases the risk of civilian harm, while contributing to addressing violent extremism. It is a novel risk-reduction approach comprising concrete measures to ensure that government forces fully integrate international human rights and humanitarian laws into the planning and conduct of their operations and thus minimise adverse consequences for civilian populations.

President Mahamadou Issoufou. The panel convened for this purpose will make recommendations on ways to "foster international engagement and map out responses to the region's complex challenges at hand."[127] When announcing the panel, UN Secretary General António Guterres noted the compounding effect of climate change on peace and security issues, declaring that "if nothing is done, the effects of terrorism, violent extremism and organized crime will be felt far beyond the region and the African continent." While this assessment is ongoing, two complementary approaches are working to address some of these issues in West Africa and the Sahel: the Accra Initiative aims to reduce the spill-over effects of violent extremism via a collaborative security mechanism; and the Africa Facility to Support Inclusive Transitions has been working to deepen democratic governance across the continent.

Before he was ousted in a coup in July 2023, President Bazoum of Niger declared that "terrorism and crime are closely linked with climate change."[128] The problems of the Sahel run extraordinarily deep, and are related to a combination of bad governance (from colonial times until now) and natural causes: the harshness of the terrain, environmental degradation, population growth, desperate poverty, extremism, smuggling, migration. Several countries have experienced military coups in recent years (including Burkina Faso, Mali and Niger) bringing to power militaries who have even less motivation and experience to resolve issues in any other way barring the commission of further human rights violations. These violations have made many of the region's problems even more acute. The effects of climate change have had a similar impact. Mark Lowcock, the UN's Humanitarian Coordinator described the Sahel in 2020 as "a canary in the coalmine of our warming planet", with the region suffering both drought and severe flooding. He added that "there is a totally inadequate level of international effort in helping these countries adapt to climate change." The EU Special Envoy similarly referred to the "perfect storm" of crises in the Sahel.[129]

This appalling combination of political instability, religious extremism, and humanitarian crisis has engulfed the Sahel region. Together, they are spilling people beyond national frontiers, and across continents. Although this is a tragedy for those affected, most of the population in Western countries continues to disregard how their own fate might be linked to the Sahel's. For such people, the crisis in the Sahel is perhaps the number one example in the world of how what they have hitherto considered to be a 'secondary' problem may quickly become a 'primary' one. This will be explored in Chapter 4.

4 Migration: the massive new challenge

The dominant feature of the next two decades and more is likely to be migration on a scale that has never been experienced before. It is neither exaggerated nor alarmist to point this out. Compounding the enormity of the issue itself will be the nature of the response of the non-migrating world. A large part of the population movement will be a result of climate change, but the effects of armed conflict will often continue to be the deciding factor. These will not be the only drivers behind people's decisions to move: digitalisation in its various forms, whether reflected in changes to labour patterns because of automation and AI, as well as social media showing higher qualities of life, will also play a role.[130] [i]

How the countries of final destination will be impacted by all this migration will be a huge challenge for everyone concerned. It might be helpful to identify for whom climate change has what may be termed 'primary' effects, and for whom the effects are rather 'secondary'. As

i As the British Minister for Development, Andrew Mitchell, has put it, "The most significant issue in the world is migration, because everyone has a mobile phone and everyone knows there's a better life 100, 200, 500 miles away. If you don't build safer, stronger, less conflict-ridden, more prosperous lives where they live, they're going to move."[131]

one climate expert, Jonny West, has put it, "primary is what you feel when your environment gets stuffed. Secondary is what you feel when someone else's does, and when they then leave home and come and try to live next to you, bringing all the issues often associated with such movements, and affecting political and social fault lines that already exist in your society."[132]

The relative timing and scale of these two sets of phenomena is significant when it comes to a recurrent theme of this book: the need to integrate thinking about conflict with the climate crisis. After all, it is unlikely that northern Europe will suffer a radical degradation of its environment or living standards in the next decade. But it is very possible that the political order in Europe will be further destabilised by migration and the effects of 'faraway' conflicts where climate is playing a major role (i.e. in what may be considered 'secondary' terms for Europeans). If one million arrivals could convulse the liberal political settlement in much of Europe in 2015, what would ten million do? Given that most people in developed and more temperate countries are not closely involved in or concerned by distant conflicts, where climate change often inflicts its worst damage, it is understandable that the subjects we are dealing with here may appear somewhat remote if viewed only through the 'primary' effects lens. Thus, it is the issue of climate migration, existential though it is for the millions who will have to undertake it, that may provide the pathway for bringing the topic of conflict and climate change (otherwise of 'secondary' importance in richer countries) into mainstream discussion in regions that have not yet been so impacted by altered weather patterns.

By 2070, areas where the mean annual temperature exceeds 29°C could cover one fifth of the Earth's landmass, up from its current small area of under one per cent, at which point would affect 3.5 billion people worldwide.[133] Such a high average temperature (and of course it will not be experienced as an average) will make vast areas of the world uninhabitable. Not only will this greatly reduce productivity, particularly of cereal crops[134] – as happened following recent heatwaves in India and China which killed large numbers of livestock too – but it also poses extreme risks to human health.

When "wet-bulb" temperatures[i] reach 32°C and above, the body's capacity for thermo-regulation is overwhelmed, making any kind of outdoor activity potentially deadly. These temperatures are no longer the preserve of some distant future. In the first half of 2022, wet-bulb temperatures of 32°C and above were recorded in Chennai, Ahmedabad, and Kolkata in India. Across India and Pakistan, at least 90 people died during the heatwave, while forest fires spread and a glacial lake outburst flooded parts of northern Pakistan. Meanwhile, in China, temperatures of over more than 40°C caused severe damage to roads, and extreme floods displaced almost half a million people.[137] Heat levels are far from the only climate change-related cause of migration; others include floods (from torrential rain, melting glaciers or sea-level rise), storms, and the loss of agricultural land to either desertification or salination.

The Indian sub-continent is at particular risk of many of these extremes. In addition to the human health impact of heatwaves, the economic damage can also be great, with the World Bank estimating that the 2022 heatwaves had led – via perished livestock and lost working days – to a 15 per cent loss of agricultural output in both India and Pakistan. That same year, Pakistan also suffered catastrophic floods after heavy rainfall and rapid melting of its glaciers, with immense areas of the country inundated and a bill of US$30 billion in damage and economic loss. The World Weather Attribution Group estimated that the country's monsoon rains were 50 per cent more intense than they would have been had it not been for climate change. Even before the dual afflictions, Pakistan was often in political crisis marked by army coups and violent extremism. It is hard not to conclude that climate change will have a growing impact on political tensions and social and religious conflict in Pakistan.[138]

---

i 'Wet-bulb' temperatures are often used as a measure of the danger posed by extreme heat, combining temperature and humidity. This is the method of measuring temperature by wrapping a wet cloth around the thermometer, simulating the process of sweating. It means the reading can account for the cooling strategy employed by the body in hot conditions. In cities, the lack of vegetation, the tarmac and the reverse heat from air conditioners can combine to produce the 'urban-heat-island effect', often worse in poorer areas that also have more polluted air – not for nothing has the term 'climate apartheid' been coined. Heat already kills more Americans than any other type of weather.[135] In his book *The Heat Will Kill You First*, Jeff Goodell wrote: "a heatwave is a predatory event, one that culls out the most vulnerable people."[136]

In such conditions, migration often becomes (and as temperatures continue to rise, it will increasingly become) the most natural response, and one which itself demonstrates a form of resilience. By the end of May 2022, the number of people in the world forcibly displaced breached 100 million.[139] Of this figure, more than 32 million needed to move because of weather-related phenomena such as drought, floods, and storms – and this is before we have even reached 1.5°C of warming.[i][141] By mid-century, the number of people displaced by climate change is likely to dwarf this figure. A report by the World Bank in 2021 estimated that another 216 million people may be forcibly displaced by climate change by 2050. Looking at the combined threat of conflict and natural disasters, the Institute for Economics and Peace predicted 1.2 billion migrants.[142] In either scenario, climate-induced migration will place a heavy burden on resource management and governance structures, and where these are already under siege as a result of protracted conflict, the risks will only increase – although some commentaries see some potentially positive consequences too.[ii] It should be added that if, as appears to be the case, global heating occurs more quickly than previously expected, these numbers will be reached much sooner than 2050.[144]

Research on the links between climate change, migration and conflict is complex and even controversial. Isolating climate change as a driver of migration is difficult, and identifying the specific role of climate in the decisions of migrants who are also trying to escape from – and may in turn later provoke further – conflict is even more so.[145] However, some progress has been made. In India, research

---

i Evidence from other parts of the animal kingdom has relevance for humans. Various mammals are now moving into the Arctic region, including rabbit, caribou and beaver. Meanwhile, some species already native to that region (such as musk ox and Arctic fox) feel compelled to move ever further towards the North Pole, increasingly finding less inhabitable territory. In a parallel process, some species of birds, insects and trees in the Amazon are moving onto, and then up, mountains to escape the heat. Of course, there is a very finite limit (both in latitude and altitude) to how far they can all go.[140]

ii Another estimate is that over 3 billion people could be living in regions and areas that are uninhabitable by 2100. But some see some upsides to migration. Assuming future migration causes large numbers of subsistence farmers to move to cities, this would slow the birth rate in countries such as Niger, which has the highest such rate in the world, and lead to the affected population probably finding better work, healthcare and schools. According to a survey by IOM, 75 per cent of people in Niger believe that climate change has made it harder to grow crops and raise cattle.[143]

has shown how irregular rainfall patterns can drive migration and civil unrest. As people are displaced into urban areas, riots become increasingly common occurrences, particularly in areas where there is disaffection with the central government.[146] It is a similar situation in Amman, Jordan, where an influx of Syrian refugees put so much additional pressure on water resources that it contributed to the government's decision to push for a contentious water-for-solar deal with neighbouring Israel in 2022, sparking a wave of protests among communities angered by Israeli settlements and repressive policies towards the Palestinians in the West Bank.[147]

There are similarities between the debate on the direct link between climate change and conflict, on the one hand, and the discourse around climate and migration, on the other. Many analysts believe that climate change is a causal component in both conflict and migration. Others challenge this assumption. But there are aspects that nobody denies. We know that conflict often leads to migration – and that such migration can produce further conflict. Recently, we have also started to see people being forcibly displaced by climate change impacts, such as sea-level rise. In other words, it seems that only when all three of these issues are put together (not when it is a matter of just two of them) that the links become questioned. But even some of the people who have questioned the extent to which climate has *hitherto* contributed to either conflict or migration are less certain that climate – as the rate of change increases – will not play a bigger role *in future*.[148]

Be that as it may, the current ambivalence in research does not seem to reflect the growing impact of climate change on migration. As temperatures rise and conditions deteriorate in the coming decades, it is hard not to conclude that migration flows will increase, adding to the risk of violent confrontations in several ways. In a society that is already in conflict (or was until recently), the impact of a major climate-related drought coming on top of such conflict could lead to migration. This could be either direct (as affected communities seek a less challenging environment), or indirect, if the drought triggers local conflicts that ultimately inform the decision to migrate. Research has been undertaken on the reasons behind migration, and the influence they have on migrants' reception.[149] One finding is that as extreme weather events and prolonged droughts become more frequent, particular attention will need to be paid to areas with a history of violent conflict where governance institutions are already overstretched.

Where do most climate migrants go? Most research to date has focused on intra-state movement. And far greater numbers have indeed remained in their own countries even after leaving their homes. But in future, as current (less affected) destinations within the same country also suffer from climate change, or when cities become completely overwhelmed, we can expect to see greater migration flows not just within countries but mainly across borders and seas.

The outcomes may well be momentous, especially if the number of climate refugees reaches tens or even hundreds of millions. In 2015, Europe was confronted with a dual challenge. The first was humanitarian, with over a million people who had fled the wars in Syria, Afghanistan, and Libya arriving in Europe to seek asylum. The routes that many were forced to take exposed them to the risk of human trafficking and torture. Even had there not been strong Western involvement in the prosecution of these conflicts, many believed there was a moral imperative to help asylum seekers as they reached European shores. Why that help was not immediately forthcoming highlights the second challenge: the political dilemma posed by mass immigration.

While German Chancellor Angela Merkel issued her refugee-welcoming policy "*Wir schaffen das*" (We can do it), far-right groups in Germany, including the AfD, capitalised on growing anti-immigrant sentiment in the country. Elsewhere, in Sweden, Prime Minister Stefan Löfven boldly declared: "My Europe takes in refugees ... My Europe doesn't build walls." They accepted 163,000 refugees. However, as in Germany but more so, the Swedish sense of responsibility and willingness to accept migrants soon started to wane. The rhetoric that was once the preserve of the far right became more mainstream and enabled the election of the Sweden Democrats in 2022 – a party that many Swedes had considered toxic owing to their nationalist-exceptionalist views. This phenomenon was repeated in other countries, including those that took in far fewer refugees than either Germany or Sweden that year.

Migration was one of the issues that led to the Brexit result in 2016, both in the context of Eastern Europeans working in the UK and fears of immigration from Turkey (a deceit based on the unfounded claim that Turkey would shortly be joining the EU); it was also influenced by what was presented as the chaotic influx of refugees into continental Europe the previous year.[150] In France, it has been key to the support for Marine Le Pen's far-right party. Fear of Mediterranean migrants was a major factor in the rise of Italy's Matteo Salvini, who also pushed to withdraw his country from the EU (although Giorgia Meloni, who became Prime Minster in 2022, while sharing Salvini's hostility to immigrants, is not anti-EU). Hungary's Prime Minister Victor Orbán, too, has drawn on the migrant crisis to legitimise his increasingly repressive and isolationist regime that seems to thrive on baiting Brussels. The prospect of parties and movements such as these taking power continues to haunt policymakers throughout Europe and makes a welcoming environment for refugees — fleeing climate change, conflict or both — unlikely for the foreseeable future.

In some places, those at the forefront of the anti-immigrant movement use environmental arguments. This may seem ironic given that anti-immigrant leaders and their supporters are among those most sceptical that climate change is even happening, let alone a problem that requires immense political and social effort. Le Pen's party in France has campaigned on what some have called 'ecological localism', shamelessly comparing immigrants to foreign invasive species, using slogans like "Borders are the environment's greatest ally: it is through them that we will save the planet".[151] [i] Such thinking, which had some origins in Nazi Germany, is as far from a peaceful conception of nature as it is possible to imagine.

---

i In what would be a surprise to few people, similar sentiments were expressed in Germany in the 1930s, and by some thinkers cited by the Nazis from preceding decades, who believed that the origins of true love for the Fatherland were derived from a love for (specifically German) nature and landscape.

It is not just in Europe where campaigns of this type have a relationship both to climate change and racism. In Tunisia, birthplace of the Arab Spring of 2011, drought-caused water shortages have ravaged the country's grain crop and caused the government to fear they might provoke another round of major civil unrest. In early 2023, President Kais Saied's incendiary speeches contributed to a violent surge of attacks against migrants from sub-Saharan Africa who had left their home countries partly because of climate change. Many saw this as part of an attempt to distract attention from the dire economic situation of Tunisia. African migrants in the country were accused (in a curious parallel to Donald Trump's repeated attacks on Muslims and Hispanics as 'invaders' of the US, and other adherents to the 'Great Replacement Theory') of being part of a plot to dilute Tunisia's Arab identity, and were then hunted down and attacked by mobs.[152]

Although some on the far right may be 'pro-environment' in the limited sense that they may favour conservation of areas of natural beauty and particular species of animals, appeals to protect 'local ecology' as a reason to keep out foreigners and immigrants seems a largely cynical exercise to increase support for their main agenda. That agenda has an additional ironic component. Although far-right parties generally express extreme dislike and fear of immigrants, with frequent claims that such newcomers are violent and conflict-prone, they in fact find immigration deeply advantageous politically. It is when immigrants arrive in large numbers, giving the far right an opportunity to denounce them and the governing parties that allegedly encourage such immigration, that the populist anti-immigrant parties know they can prosper electorally. Violence against the newcomers is often the result, as is the growth of social conflict within the host communities. In September 2023, Pope Francis decried what he called the "fanaticism of indifference", [153] referring to some Europeans' response to migrants and their terrifying journeys that he felt were profoundly inhumane. The real problem though is that indifference is far from the worst problem – the active hatred directed at them, whipped up cynically, and sometimes turning to violence, is an even greater tragedy.

How the 2015 and 2016 migrant crisis played out in Europe (and also the US, with the election that year of the migrant-hating and climate change-denying Donald Trump) was clearly regarded by some as a fruitful new avenue for potential destabilisation. This view appears to have been especially prevalent in Moscow which was accused at the time of weaponising migration through its attacks on Syrian civilians forcing them to leave their destroyed homes. Such weaponisation is likely to continue, both from that quarter and from others. These include President Recep Tayyip Erdoğan, who can see the effect that migration has on Europe and negotiates with the EU accordingly, playing Turkey's strong card that derives from hosting millions of Syrian refugees and the threat to 'open the floodgates' and let them move to Europe.

The 2024 European elections will be important both on climate issues and migration – with right-wing parties across the continent seeking to tighten still further the system of immigration into the EU, at the same time as pushing back on the 'green agenda'. Though Ukraine is the biggest external issue currently facing both the EU and Russia, the latter supports the views of the European right-wing parties on both migrants and environmentalist measures, seeking to use them to promote discord in Western countries.

To Vladimir Putin and his government, migration and climate change provide new avenues to exert power and to pursue their perceived self-interest. His efforts to drive migration as a means of destabilising the West, paired with his regressive stance on climate change, are part of a clear line of thinking. That he sees them as complementary weapons in his arsenal is increasingly clear. Libya is a case in point.

In 2019, Libya was still caught up in a civil war. Its instability and the absence of government authorities since 2011 had made it an attractive route for migrants fleeing to Europe. Even beforehand, Colonel Muammar Gaddafi's government, which came to a singularly brutal and undignified end in 2011, had encouraged approximately 1.8 million migrants to come to Libya from sub-Saharan countries that were affected by both conflict and environmental degradation.[154] In the civil war that followed in this extremely water-scarce nation, those immigrants were targeted, in many cases with extreme cruelty. Nearly 30,000 sought to migrate again, this time northwards over the Mediterranean Sea[155] – thus becoming climate and conflict refugees for a second time.[156] These events did not take place without the influence of external forces, however.

Having seen the effects of Syrian migration on Europe in 2015 and 2016, Putin authorised the deployment of the Wagner Group of Russian mercenaries to Libya in 2018. Just as they had achieved in Central African Republic, Mali and other places, these fighters succeeded in deepening political instability and undermining state presence. In doing so, more people were encouraged or felt compelled to try to cross the Mediterranean. Once in Europe, according to the Kremlin calculus, these new immigrants would contribute to destabilisation in Western Europe.

An even more blatant demonstration of this came in 2021, when the Russian government used its suzerainty over Belarus to channel migrants from the crises in Afghanistan and Iraq to the borders of Poland, Latvia, and Lithuania. There was little effort to conceal the state's involvement and it is widely accepted that this was an attempt to re-create the conditions that had produced such political dividends for the Moscow leadership in Western Europe in 2015 and 2016.

The idea that Russia would drive the climate crisis for its own ends is not easy to prove conclusively. However, there are several factors that make it highly credible. Russia has less to lose from climate change than any other country, and as a petro-state more to lose from a move away from fossil fuels. On the first point, more than 60 per cent of Russian territory is covered in permafrost – a layer of earth that remains below freezing point year-round. This creates extremely inhospitable living conditions, offering (for now) no real opportunity for agriculture, although the loss of that revenue has been more than compensated for by the oil and gas beneath the surface.

As it thaws, however, it will present opportunities particularly with regards to agriculture. Over time, once thawing is complete, land previously covered in ice will reach an equilibrium, allowing new building and large-scale cultivation of cereals. As well as the increase in available land for agriculture, the opening up of Arctic trading routes will create new opportunities for Russia to profit and boost its influence over world food markets, not to mention its strategic and military standing.[i]

Starting in 2010, Russia's dominant position in world food markets had an unintended impact in advancing its perceived strategic interests. After a particularly dry summer, combined with a series of wildfires, President Putin banned exports of Russian wheat – one of the factors behind the subsequent threefold increase in global food prices.[158] This served the purpose of shoring up Russia's grain supplies. Putin clearly loathes all protest movements that have risen up against his allies, and the Arab Spring that erupted in 2011 was a cause of deep concern to him. On the other hand, as events turned out, the grain price rise (that he had contributed to) and the insurrections it partly caused had what was for Putin the beneficial side-effect of providing a major Russian military and diplomatic entry point into the Middle East, especially in the Syrian context. And beyond the shift in the regional military balance in Russia's favour, it created an influx of migration into Europe, with major political consequences.

Throughout his incumbency, the Russian leader and his government have made known their intentions on mitigating (or profiting from) the effects of climate change. Back in 2003, Putin mockingly suggested: "an increase of two or three degrees wouldn't be so bad for a northern country like Russia. We could spend less on fur coats, and the grain harvest would go up." Russia's consistently negative voting record on climate action at the UN is also indicative.[159] But it is perhaps less on a direct climate issue, and more on food scarcity (whether caused by climate change, or in this case the invasion of Ukraine) that

---

i There are significant downsides to permafrost thaw. Its thaw threatens to create a negative feedback loop by releasing methane, a greenhouse gas about 25 times more potent than carbon dioxide. As the gas reaches the atmosphere, it catalyses the global warming process. In addition to its impact on the climate, permafrost thaw also destabilises the land above it. Back in 2016, an oil storage tank in the city of Norilsk in Northern Siberia ruptured due to such thaw. 21,000 tonnes of diesel were released, seeping into the ground and colouring the nearby Ambarnaya River red. The clean-up operation is likely to cost billions of roubles.[157] Incidents like these are becoming more and more common, but neither they, nor the release of vast quantities of methane, are likely to counterbalance what Putin considers to be the strategic benefits of climate change.

the deliberate strategy of encouraging migrants to flee to Europe has been spelled out most clearly. In 2022, amid the food shortages sparked by Russia's invasion of Ukraine, the head of Russia's Security Council, Nikolai Patrushev, observed: "The world is gradually falling into an unprecedented food crisis. Tens of millions of people in Africa or in the Middle East will turn out to be on the brink of starvation – because of the West. In order to survive, they will flee to Europe." Patrushev drew what was for him the ultimately wishful conclusion: "I'm not sure Europe will survive the crisis."[160]

That point is clearly one of the current leadership's primary strategic goals, and almost all the evidence from scientists and sociologists suggests that intensified climate change will lead to even larger numbers of refugees fleeing to Europe. It is therefore hard to avoid the conclusion that disastrous climate change is seen by at least one major global player as being in its long-term strategic interests.[i]

For this reason, if not many others, the Russian leadership may be feeling complacent about the future. It is widely recognised that throughout history, people have been prompted to migrate not only in response to environmental problems, but as a means of escaping poverty, deprivation and armed conflict.

The example of Libya shows what can happen when communities and governments come under immense pressure from what is a new, challenging and increasingly acute triple nexus: climate change, migration and conflict.[ii] Without international governance mechanisms equipped to respond to it, the outcomes for the displaced will be infinitely worse.

---

i See, for instance, in a report released by the White House: "Russia also sees some benefits in the destabilizing effects of large-scale migration to the EU, particularly as it relates to the rise of xenophobia and political parties sceptical of the European project and the broader liberal order. Despite likely challenges around the effects of weather extremes, including Arctic warming, flooding and increased forest fires, Russia may on balance benefit from climate change via the expansion of areas available for cultivation, resource extraction, and previously inaccessible maritime routes. Russia may also seek to bolster its global image by accepting certain refugees and migrants, even as this potential influx of climate refugees would likely exacerbate existing tensions around labour migration in the country."[161]

ii This is not to be confused with what is known in the UN as the 'HDP Triple Nexus', bringing together humanitarian, development and peace activities.

The cornerstone of international protection for those seeking asylum is the 1951 Convention Relating to the Status of Refugees. That document, which has formed the basis of international law on displacement since World War II, sets out the rights of any individual "fleeing persecution"; this may be "for reasons of race, religion, nationality, membership of a particular social group or political opinion". Although broad, this definition still does not include environmental factors, even though there has been talk of 'environmental refugees' for the past 40 years. Indeed, the head of the UN Environment Programme at the time, Essam El- Hinnawi, wrote about them in 1985, mentioning as examples some who had been forced to "abandon arid land when their cattle have grazed the last blade of grass".[162]

Climate change does not constitute grounds for claiming refugee status, as one key criterion – persecution – has not been met. In everyday terms, persecution has connotations of deliberate targeting by a perpetrator – a conscious action designed to undermine the security of individuals or a group. But when it comes to climate change and environmental issues, the perpetrator is less obvious. Rather, climate change is a process carried out by a faceless phenomenon.[i] Unless international refugee law changes to recognise climate change or climate injustice as creating refugee status, or as forms of persecution, people fleeing what may feel like persecution by the environment fall into a desperate legal vacuum: they have nowhere liveable to return to, but also have nowhere permissible to go.[164]

Regional agreements on refugees in place since 1951 have been more inclusive and may provide some inspiration for the current international legal framework. The Organisation for African Unity Refugee Convention (1969) and the Cartagena Declaration (1984) not only include the definition of refugees based on persecution, but also state that individuals may be considered as refugees if they have been displaced by events "seriously disturbing public order" even if they do not meet the (intentional) persecution criterion.

---

i Despite the fact that 100 companies have produced 71 per cent of the fossil fuels that have caused climate change.[163]

Climate-induced environmental disasters may well qualify as an example of such events.

UNHCR – the UN organisation responsible for refugees – has indicated that climate-induced migration may be considered under the existing Refugee Convention. In its 2020 "Strategic Framework for Climate Action", it referred to climate change as "the defining crisis of our time" and suggested that the existing refugee law may be applicable to climate-induced displacement. A follow-up memo later the same year stated that "people fleeing in the context of adverse consequences of climate change and disasters may have valid claims to refugee status."[165] Four years earlier, the UN's Human Rights Committee had concluded, in a case brought against New Zealand, that states have a duty to refrain from sending asylum seekers back to another state in which either their life or their physical integrity would be seriously endangered due to climate harms.[166] [i]

This is definite progress, and it should be welcomed and supported. Enabling access to legal protections for migrants fleeing climate disaster would help prevent the kind of human rights abuses that all too many are subjected to.[ii] But as with discussions of climate and security in the UN Security Council, any major advancement along these lines will be subject to intense political pressure – and not just from the Russia-China-India axis that blocked movement in 2021 on treating climate change as a security issue. In the case of recognised refugees, there seems to be little hope, for now, that the current anti-immigration groundswell in the United States and Europe will permit support for a significantly broader interpretation of the 1951 definition of refugees.

---

i The International Organization for Migration has moved in a similar direction, stating that "contemporary migration governance, policy and practice must reflect the significance of environmental, disaster and climate change factors on human mobility."

ii It should be noted that refugee schemes will be no panacea, however. As the recent example of New Zealand's experimental climate refugee visa scheme shows, this may not always been in the interests of affected people. Some argued in this case that by accepting refugee status, they felt subject to marginalising treatment, contrary to what they would have experienced had they been offered 'migrant' status. Indeed, what many Pacific Islanders asked for instead were the resources for adaptation, and that big emitting countries meaningfully engage in mitigation.[167]

Nevertheless, progress at the international level may also be matched in domestic courts. A recent study of asylum cases in German courts involving Afghans, Iraqis, and Somalis showed that as part of the proceedings, they analysed the effects that natural disasters in their countries (which had led to drastic food and water shortages) would have on the plaintiffs. The study concluded that these cases indicated how protection for people displaced in the context of climate change and natural disasters might be provided outside the Refugee Convention, using existing human rights law to benefit persons displaced due to climate harm.[168]

The impacts of climate change, conflict and migration will be felt well beyond the regions from which these families and communities have been compelled to migrate. In a number of instances, as so often with refugees, some will bring great benefits to their host nations. In many others, not least because of the likely scale of the migration, this influx will be accompanied by a major social and political dislocation that could shake the democratic foundations of many nation states. Be it due to the lack of political representation of refugees, the rise of populism or the lack of legal clarity, this will be difficult terrain to navigate.

As the planet continues to heat up, at some point in the coming decades, if not sooner, the more developed countries are going to be obliged to accept significantly larger numbers of refugees from the lesser developed but more climate-affected countries. The destination countries, however, have neither prepared domestically for such arrivals nor acted to invest overseas in the adaptation and resilience mechanisms that could be expected to slow that flow. Although the political difficulties involved in such decisions will be immense, it is to be hoped that far-sighted figures will emerge who will seek to prepare their respective electorates for this probability. To reduce the likelihood of political conflict and violence in recipient countries, there will be a need to prepare host populations through systematic forms of peace education and inter-cultural dialogue.

In addition to arguments relating to moral obligation, human rights and climate justice, crucial self-interested factors will also be in play. In many countries, working age populations are shrinking. By 2050, the percentage of the population over 65 years old may reach nearly 40 per cent in parts of Europe and East Asia.[169] Recognising the growing gaps in their workforce, politicians and opinion-formers are likely to find their self-interest begins to mirror their moral responsibility (that they have so far kept fairly quiet about), and will publicise the benefits that an increase in migration will have for the host countries and communities.

One of the more far-sighted thinkers in this regard is Gaia Vince, whose 2022 book *Nomad Century: How to Survive the Climate Upheaval* envisions a world that may be up to 4 degrees hotter than before industrialisation. She depicts a world of "drowned cities; stagnant seas; a crash in biodiversity; intolerable heatwaves; entire countries becoming uninhabitable; widespread hunger." In these circumstances, it is not surprising that hundreds of millions of people may be compelled to move. But Vince proposes – convincingly – that migration should not just permanently be seen as a security and economic threat; rather it should be seen as the solution.

Migrants can bring great benefits. The increasing vibrancy of the Neukölln neighbourhood in Berlin, for example, has been suggested as an example of new economic opportunities being created as a result of the arrival of refugees from Syria. One review of Vince's book concluded that she optimistically did not dwell on the scenario whereby the world fails to cope with the massive dislocation envisaged by the higher temperatures, but – in such a scenario – the result would be "widespread and perpetual conflict across the world, and a tragic new chapter in human history."[170]

Before tens of millions of migrants or refugees begin to flee from their homelands (either from the direct effects of climate change, or from conflicts that have been exacerbated by climate change), there is an obvious need to increase assistance to the most affected countries. This would mean substantially increased financial and technical support for adaptation measures on a scale sufficient to induce would-be migrants to believe that they still have a chance of leading a reasonable life by remaining in their own countries, despite the deterioration of so much of their environmental and social infrastructure.

Perhaps no sector of the economy is more suitable for adaptation support than agriculture, given some analysts' conclusion that the most important among all non-conflict motivations for migration is any given region's incapacity to feed itself.[171] As the Oxford analyst, Adam Parr, has put it: "Just as a failing agricultural system damages society and the environment, so an improving system is a 'force multiplier' for progress, underpinning all the SDGs."

An example of this approach is the System of Rice Intensification (SRI), an 'agroecological' solution whose benefits include increased grain yield, enhanced micronutrient content, higher income for farmers, water conservation, and lower emissions (especially methane). Mali is one of several countries that have successfully promoted SRI and have also adopted it in the country's Nationally Determined Contributions (NDCs). Mali produces about 2 million tonnes of rice a year on a million hectares, but when SRI is used the yields are tripled. From being a small importer of rice, Mali has ambitions to become a major producer and exporter, which could be achieved without more land being used. The UK's Foreign, Commonwealth and Development Office (FCDO) has recently funded a two-year SRI programme in the Nigerian states of Kano, Kaduna and Jigawa that trained 45,000 farmers over 15,000 hectares. On average, yields doubled, greenhouse gas emissions halved, and returns increased six-fold.[172]

Another approach is to encourage African farmers to move from producing rice towards millet, which is more nutritious and requires less water, an important consideration given that the irrigation of rice paddy fields is responsible for 12 per cent of the total global emissions of methane gas.[173] As one proponent puts it, more sustainable cultivation and increasing yields would give farmers higher incomes, thereby both helping them to adapt to climate change and also to contribute to it less. SMI (the SRI equivalent for millet) has also demonstrated improved yields and environmental impact compared with conventional methods.

Even in areas where these kinds of programmes are more difficult to implement, SRI has achieved success. In Mali, Nepal, and Afghanistan, farmers have welcomed trainers on SRI in areas controlled by insurgent groups, enabling food security benefits to reach those usually most vulnerable.[174]

Parr concludes that agricultural development programmes such as SRI and SMI offer benefits for both mitigation and adaptation, while improving food security and taking pressure off scarce land and water resources. It has also been shown to benefit women, as the governments of Mali and India have noted. Overall, it is a logical place to start for any serious effort to tackle climate insecurity and to promote human security at source, in other words before large numbers of people conclude that migration is the only solution to the dual problems of conflict and climate.

It would be an act of basic justice for the richer and less climate-affected states to take serious (which inevitably means well-funded) actions to encourage would-be migrants to remain in their home regions, given the origin of the emissions that has caused the climate crisis in the first place. But it would also be one of enlightened self-interest, at least as they themselves define it, especially on the part of those who loudly claim it is against their 'interests' to allow large numbers of climate migrants to arrive in their countries.

For climate migrants to be dissuaded from leaving their own countries, not only do carbon emissions need to be rapidly reduced, when the long-term mitigation side of the equation is considered. In addition, substantial shorter-term investment will be required in the worst-affected countries (which also include those in conflict) to ensure that their populations can earn a living in new and adaptive ways. This will apply not just to those suffering from climate change itself, but also those where the energy transition (in response to climate change) will be felt especially hard.

5 The energy transition: another source of conflict

Since the Industrial Revolution of the 19th century, fossil fuels and the energy they release have underpinned the global economy. The development benefits that resulted are obvious enough. It is only in recent years that policy-makers throughout the world have come to recognise that these benefits (particularly for the countries that industrialised first) have come at a massive cost – for the world as a whole, but for poor countries most of all. And this is because of a terrible and unjust irony.

Many under-developed nations are situated in regions where climate change is disproportionately intense, but at the same time have historically contributed little to the accumulated carbon emissions which have caused the climate change that is destroying their ways of life.[i] Countries such as Pakistan, which suffered massive floods in August 2022, and Somalia, which faces drought-induced famine, have received almost none of the development benefits derived from earlier

i Yet another factor reinforcing this injustice is that a significant amount of the capital that enabled the rich countries to develop their emissions-producing technologies and industries actually derived from the profits from slave labour in the New World.

emissions, yet they are now obliged to pay the highest price for the gains still enjoyed by other – higher-emitting – nations.

Necessitated by climate change, our relationship with energy is finally changing – relatively fast given that we are talking about seismic global changes in attitudes, but at the same time nowhere near quick enough. To mitigate the growing impact of carbon emissions, the global energy network is shifting from oil, coal and gas towards more renewable and low-carbon sources. While this may represent a positive shift and lead to a much-needed reduction in emissions, it also has the potential to destabilise our societies in profound ways.

The push for more sustainable policies has already produced instances of civil unrest even in highly developed Western countries. In 2018, the French government imposed a tax increase on fuel with the aim of reducing fuel consumption and hence carbon emissions. But the tax burden fell hardest on people who faced price rises for their daily commutes, particularly in rural areas where a car is the only feasible means of transport. Although intended as a constructive move for climate action, the policy instead deepened social and economic divides, and gave rise to the *Gilets Jaunes* movement, civil unrest and several incidents of violence. One of the movement's slogans was *"Fin du monde? Fin du mois"*, as if to insinuate that it was only privileged environmentalist 'elites' who were concerned about such allegedly esoteric issues as the end of the world, whereas the ordinary public was more concerned about making ends meet until the next monthly pay cheque.

The unrest witnessed in France, relatively mild though it may have been, is likely to be a harbinger of other such movements elsewhere in the world in years to come.[i] This has led some to argue that

i In 2022-23, President Putin clearly hoped that, by reducing oil and gas supplies and raising prices, there would be far bigger mass protests throughout Europe, and that far-right and far-left parties would be able to harness this discontent (that would dwarf the gilets jaunes movement) to reverse NATO countries' boycott of Russian fossil fuels and their support for Ukrainian military resistance. The hope was also that it would put a stop to the energy transition towards renewables that in the long run would undercut Russia's ability to sell to its largest market, the EU. But European governments moved rapidly to reduce the impact of high prices on their citizens, and were aided by mild early winter temperatures.[175] This meant that Putin's hopes in this area were not realised.

policies designed to mitigate climate change will — unless carefully designed — disproportionately burden lower-income households.[176]

The negative effects of climate mitigation policies can, however, be mitigated with other policies, creating a redistributive double dividend. For example, revenues raised from carbon taxes can be distributed to households so that they are income-neutral but also encourage conservation of resources; public transport can be made more available and less expensive, alleviating burdens of the kind that triggered the *Gilets Jaunes*. Unless climate policies are carefully designed and effectively communicated, they will be co-opted into a climate-sceptic narrative of the sort being promoted by populist leaders in Europe and elsewhere. These narratives of unfairness seek to exploit socio-political divides, pitting rural communities and others more reliant on cars against the perceived urban elites who favour 'net zero'. Should governments pay greater attention to the dividends that environmental taxes can create, it is likely they would find a far more receptive public.

Pushing in the opposite direction, there has also been a surge in the number of environmental protests. A number of movements, branded 'extremist' by some sectors of the media and public, are increasingly making a mark on our political debate. In early 2023, activists from the Sami indigenous community in Norway, joined by Greta Thunberg, managed to close down parts of the government in protest against a wind farm that violated the rights of the Sami people, and the ability of their reindeer herds to graze. Denouncing this particular wind project as an example of "green colonialism", Thunberg declared that the energy transition (which in general of course she strongly supports) must not take place "at the expense of indigenous people's rights".[177] Four years earlier, *Extinction Rebellion* organised an occupation of central London and disruptions to public transport, leading to chaos and arrests. Other campaigns, such as *Just Stop Oil* and *Die Letzte Generation* in Germany, have carried out similar actions, including temporary desecration of major works of art and disrupting sporting events. Such tactics are seen by some as reminiscent of the British suffragettes in their campaign for women's right to vote a century ago — actions that were deplored at the time as extremist but are now celebrated, even though they involved bombing, arson and assassination attempts (far more violent than today's environmental protests).

These protesters seemed to be trying to turn the *Gilets Jaunes'* anti-green, anti-elitist arguments on their head. They did this by using anti-elitist arguments which were, by contrast, radical green. As one of the activists arrested after throwing tomato soup over Van Gogh's "Sunflowers" (without actually damaging it) declared, "Are you more concerned about the protection of a painting, or the protection of our planet and people? The cost of living crisis is part of the cost of oil crisis. Fuel is unaffordable to millions of cold, hungry families. They can't even afford to heat a tin of soup." [178]

While many members of the public expressed sympathy with the green protesters' motives – bringing dramatic attention to the unsustainability of current social and economic models, based as they are on fossil fuels and insufficient action to reduce carbon in the atmosphere – their methods, especially when they inconvenienced thousands of commuters, led to different reactions. In the UK, for instance, the government clamped down on such protests by passing new laws to limit free speech and freedom of assembly.[179] It is perhaps unfortunate that Just Stop Oil, one of the most active of these groups, has chosen a name that misrepresents its policy demands and plays into the counter-argument that we cannot "just stop oil". In fact, *Just Stop Oil*'s demand is similar in substance (if very different in style of delivery) to that of the International Energy Agency (IEA), namely that there should be no *new* licensing of oil and gas resources. As the IEA has demonstrated, there are enough existing reserves to fuel the transition, while the development of new resources is not compatible with the Paris Agreement.

Whatever one's position on green protests and the laws that are meant to counter them, they reflect the deepening divisions and desperation in the climate debate. In countries where lifestyles are going to have to change, in some cases rapidly and quite radically, failing to address the demands and to build some form of consensus could well cause political instability. Already we are starting to see the emergence of movements for whom the non-violent protests of *Just Stop Oil* and *Extinction Rebellion* do not go far enough. At the start of 2023, there were acts of sabotage against fossil fuel infrastructure, while protesters fought riot police in the German village of Lutzerath, which had been condemned so that an open-cast coal mine could be enlarged. And there were bigger fights in Western France in April, over an attempt to sabotage a new mega-project to harvest groundwater for industrial agriculture. These protests are becoming more commonplace, which indicates, as one analysis has put it, in the longer term there may well be "a radical change in public attitudes towards potentially violent activism" – as protests appeal to a more permissive public.[180]

The more desperate the situation becomes, the more of this direct action we are likely to see. And it can be expected to lead to strong counter-actions. Already, the issue of climate change and net zero policies are being instrumentalised as an electoral 'wedge issue' in the culture wars by conservative or far-right parties in the US, UK, Spain, Netherlands and other European countries. Proposals for heat pumps, bicycle lanes, low traffic, and reduced cattle herds are presented to electorates as mortal threats both to freedom and prosperity. The Republican Presidential candidate and Governor of Florida, Ron DeSantis, has mocked on Fox News climate science as "politicization of the weather" and laws have been passed in southern US states obliging cities to use fossil fuels. As seen in Chapter 4, there is a striking correlation in many countries between those at the forefront of creating fears about migrants and those opposing measures to resist climate change. It is for this reason that commentators that are more on the left also link the two issues, with one of them, George Monbiot, writing, "The two tasks – preventing Earth system collapse and preventing the rise of the far right – are not divisible. We have no choice but to fight both forces at once." [181]

Culture wars between more radical greens and the 'anti-woke' warriors of the West, even when they lead to limited cases of civil conflict, is far from the only – or the most dramatic – way in which the energy transition may threaten stability. The fossil fuel-funded economies in the Middle East, North Africa and elsewhere have for decades operated on the basis of an informal social contract. Goods and services, funded by exports of oil and gas, are offered in exchange for the population's acquiescence in the face of authoritarian and often corrupt government.[182] With the erosion of fuel rents precipitated by the energy transition, the stability of this form of social contract is at risk. The state will no longer be able to provide the same services, and citizens will understandably protest these losses, possibly demanding greater freedoms at the same time.[i]

Iraq is an example of a country where the vast bulk of government revenue is derived from oil exports. Given the immense wealth that has long accrued to Iraq from its large-scale oil production, one might have thought the country would have the capacity to handle the adaptation challenges from climate change – at least when compared to countries that have not earned hundreds of billions of dollars from the oil industry. But the legacy of the Baathist dictatorship, and the wars started either by Saddam Hussein (against Iran and Kuwait, plus the repression of Iraqi Kurdish and Shiite communities) or by the US-led coalition and later ISIS, together with decades of endemic corruption, have combined to produce a weak state that provides deeply inadequate services.[184] This resulting inability to properly handle both the devastating impact of climate change and the energy transition necessitated by climate change may have stark consequences for Iraq's relationship with its citizens and for inter-communal conflict.

In countries dependent on an informal social contract of this nature, political tensions are already high after the Arab Spring. If the transition is poorly managed by fossil fuel economies, it threatens to bring rises in unemployment, social and political fracture, and violent repression in response.[185] Moreover, given their heavy dependence on food imports, countries in this region are likely to become even more susceptible to global food price fluctuations due to their governments'

---

i Though not a matter of cheap fuel, a similar 'perk' traded by some governments in exchange for quiescent loyalty, has been cheap water rates in some of the most water-deficient places on the planet. This reduces incentives for individuals to save water, makes water provision even harder, and has forced people to the streets in protest. Throughout the summer of 2018, there were large demonstrations in southern Iraq, angered by the lack of water, electricity and jobs, leading to some civilian deaths at the hands of militias and soldiers.[183]

lack of resources – a phenomenon already recognised as a contributory factor in the emergence of the Arab Spring.[186]

In the early 2010s, a severe drought hit the grain-producing areas in Russia, Ukraine and China. With the world's breadbaskets limited in their capacity to supply grain, global prices shot up from US$157 to US$326 per metric tonne in the years between 2010 and 2011.[187] Eight of the top ten grain-importing states in the world are located in the Middle East and North Africa region. For the five years leading up to 2010, they had been subjected to a 'once-in-a-generation' drought. When the global price of grain doubled, governments in Syria and Egypt in particular were unable to secure supplies of bread for their citizens, exacerbating the food insecurity already created by the longer-term droughts being experienced in the Middle East at the same time. The relationship between citizens and governments continued to sour, eventually triggering widespread riots, which turned violent in many areas. It is worth noting that both of these governments were then earning revenues from oil, as was Libya to an even greater extent. With such revenues likely to diminish in the coming years, governments will be even less able to absorb these price shocks.

Cases like these demonstrate some of the risks of depending on fossil fuel revenue. But the risks of shifting away from this income stream will not only be borne by the fossil-funded economies; nor by those facing shortages. Those who now possess an abundance of the metals and minerals needed for the transition may also face the strain. This is hardly surprising; after all, during the fossil fuel era, the presence of great fossil reserves was just as often a poisoned chalice as it was a golden ticket.

During the civil conflict in Aceh, a province on the northern tip of the Indonesian island of Sumatra, the oil and gas reserves located there became one of the focal points of the conflict. After years of repression under the Suharto-led dictatorship, the people of Aceh began to demand a greater share of the revenues from the Indonesian government. Whether this was one of the central issues in the conflict, or rather a vehicle for expressing other concerns about marginalisation, is a matter of debate. But after years of insurgency and two efforts at peace negotiations,[i] the revenue-sharing arrangement became a key part of the 2005 peace agreement.[188]

Similar issues have played a role in the political and sometimes military conflict between the Kurdistan Region in Iraq and the government in Baghdad. The question of how to share the revenue from the oil produced in the Kurdish provinces and Kirkuk has been a central component of the grievances and negotiations between the two, complicating efforts to resolve tensions on other issues such as the delineation of the disputed internal boundaries, the constitution, and the role of the security forces.

An abundance of valuable resources is assuredly not a promise of peace. There is a widespread phenomenon whereby the possession of natural resources often hinders rather than advances social progress and economic growth, broadly known as the 'resource curse'. Research over the past two decades has shown that petroleum resources in particular have had three long-term impacts: making authoritarian regimes more durable; increasing corruption; and helping to trigger violent conflicts in low- and middle-income countries.[189]

This curse is unlikely to recur in the same form when it comes to 'transition minerals'. Renewable energies tend to provide more stable revenues than oil and gas, allow for more decentralised energy infrastructure, and can create more local jobs.[190] But that is not to say they will not also pose problems. The scale of requirements for these minerals is going to be huge. The demand for copper, which is a fundamental component for electric vehicles and all consumer electronics, is expected to outstrip supply by over six million tonnes in 2030 (relative to the expected supply of 19.1 million).[191] Similarly for lithium, for which global demand is expected to reach two million tonnes by 2030, up from 345,000 in 2020.[192]

---

i Supported first by Humanitarian Dialogue (HD) and then by the Crisis Management Initiative (CMI) under the charismatic leadership of Martti Ahtisaari.

Also significant is that some of these minerals often come from fragile and conflict-affected states, and can have dangerous consequences for the regions, localities and populations concerned. The 'Blood Diamond' factor is already a significant issue, whereby minerals needed for the global move from fossil fuels will be sought after to such a degree that they may well become regarded as 'blood minerals' or 'conflict renewables' – a source both of serious human rights abuses and further geopolitical tensions. The most striking example of such tensions are between the US and China, with the former leading many of its allies into banning exports of semi-conductor technology to the latter, provoking a Chinese response of tit-for-tat export controls on strategic metals used for green technologies.[193]

Cobalt is one such mineral that may be termed as a conflict resource vital for renewable energy. It is used widely in the production of batteries for everything from smartphones to electric vehicles and energy storage technologies. Demand for these goods is surging and will continue to do so. According to one report for the European Commission, the demand for cobalt globally by 2030 will be well over double the world's current annual output of 160,000 tonnes. And while new producers will be joining the market, and while recycling of used cobalt is likely to be improved, the shortfall will for the most part be made up by existing producers.[194]

Of these existing producers, the DRC will continue to be the largest – it currently produces 70 per cent of the world's cobalt.[195] It is, however, ranked as the sixth most fragile state in the world, and the 19th most corrupt.[196] Armed groups have fought over control of the mines, while the mining itself has been carried out under horrifying conditions: children employed in the mines for less than US$2 per day; children beaten by soldiers running the mines; and the absence of protective equipment for workers handling toxic substances.[197] The revenues extracted by these groups are then used to continue the fighting and the endless destabilisation of the country. As these minerals become more sought after and therefore even more valuable, conflict over controlling these resources is almost certain to increase.

Unlike many of the other linkages between climate change and conflict discussed in this book, the conflict that comes from the energy transition is not a direct impact of the climate crisis. It is not triggered by diminishing natural resources, extreme heat or rising sea levels. Rather, it is largely dependent on the measures we take in response to those phenomena, to mitigate climate change. But even as an indirect consequence, it should not be overlooked in the climate-conflict debate.

At the global level, there is an effort to bring about a radical energy transition to reduce carbon dioxide emissions, so that further climate change can be prevented in the long term. Doing so involves drastically reducing consumption of fossil fuels, drawing down some of the carbon dioxide already in the atmosphere, while simultaneously increasing the production of low-carbon energy. All these structural changes that we must make have the potential to destabilise some societies, even if they also increase stability and growth in many places.

A major factor in determining where the energy transition poses the most significant future risks to peace and stability is the current degree of economic dependence that any given country has on fossil fuel production. According to World Bank data, revenues from fossil fuels make up the entirety of export value in Iraq, 94 per cent in Libya, and 89 per cent in Nigeria.[198] If average global temperatures are to be kept even close to the 1.5–2.0°C threshold established in the Paris Agreement, global emissions must decrease by 45 per cent by 2030, and reach net zero by 2050, according to UN figures. The quantities of fossil fuels that currently keep most countries around the world afloat will need to be radically reduced along with the revenues that they generate. How economies that depend on coal, oil and gas will handle the erosion of fuel rents will be crucial to their stability in the coming decades.

One way for such economies to minimise the coming damage from the energy transition is to diversify their revenue-making activities. Saudi Arabia, which generates almost half of its GDP from fossil fuels,[199] felt the consequences of this dependence when oil prices plummeted at the start of the Covid-19 pandemic. The government responded with stringent austerity measures, tripling the rate of value-added tax.[200] In

2016, recognising the precarious economic situation that this fossil fuel dependence created, it announced its Vision 2030 plan for economic diversification. In the past five years, it has begun to invest heavily in tourism, industry, sport and start-ups.

If successful, Vision 2030 will help Saudi Arabia avoid the destabilisation which an uncontrolled energy transition may be one of the factors in bringing about. However, it is not Saudi Arabia that risks the most from an uncontrolled energy transition. The country may be heavily dependent on oil revenue, but its state institutions are relatively strong and it has amassed an immense amount of wealth to invest in economic diversification. The same applies to other Gulf countries which also set up sovereign wealth funds that were expressly mandated to invest in non-energy or alternative energy growth sectors. Almost paradoxically, therefore, a number of the main Middle East producers of fossil fuels are now also among the largest investors in green energy technologies in the world. The result of their investments is that those Gulf sovereign wealth funds have the economic potential to benefit the energy transition of countries who are in a far less advantageous position.

The paths away from dependence on fossil fuels are likely to look quite different for states such as Iraq and Nigeria. Although these two countries are also major oil producers, they have been plagued by mismanagement and corruption, and unable to accrue sovereign wealth comparable to the Gulf countries.[201] Iraq, where 45 per cent of the total budget is spent on salaries and pensions, suffered a revenue shock at the start of the Covid-19 pandemic; as oil prices fell, it was left with insufficient funds to pay its employees and pensioners, stoking existing tensions within the country and distrust in the political institutions. The Iraqi finance minister, Ali Allawi, expressed the hope that this shock would prompt the reforms necessary to manage the energy transition, but few believe that the crisis was utilised for this purpose.

Nigeria has had similar difficulty in stimulating other domestic industries. The population relies on cheap petroleum, subsidised with US$300 million per month from the government's oil export revenues. When global oil prices plummeted in 2020, the government was unable to continue providing such cheap fuel, and the price of petroleum rose significantly. But global prices were not the only factor hurting Nigeria's fossil fuel sector. Also during this time, around 30 per cent of Nigeria's petrol was being smuggled into nearby Cameroon and Benin, where prices are higher.[202] Corruption at the National Nigerian Petroleum Corporation (NNPC) has meant that little of the wealth from fossil fuels has been reinvested into alternative economic sectors — the kind that would help compensate for a transition away from oil. In June 2023, however, the newly elected President Bola Tunubu called an end to the fossil fuel subsidy, in an effort to "save our country going under."[203] The money is earmarked for boosting reliable electricity, transport infrastructure, healthcare and education.

Reforming energy sectors in oil-producing economies will be crucial in managing the fallout from the energy transition. Richer economies will be better placed to undertake serious efforts at diversifying their sources of national revenue, as will those whose progress is not stymied by public sector or government corruption. The first tasks for states such as these will be to address the management of their fossil resources.

In Iraq, any reform or modification of the overgrown civil service will mean taking on vested interests and addressing corruption and the culture of clientelism. These have placed a heavy burden on government budgets, not to mention on communities whose access to the country's deeply inadequate public services is limited. Similarly in Nigeria, the government knows it needs to reform the NNPC to ensure that the profits that can still be drawn from fossil fuels can be reinvested in other sectors of the economy, rather than siphoned off through corruption.

As with the direct implications of climate change, governance is clearly an important factor in avoiding potential conflict arising from the indirect implications, such as the energy transition.[204] This applies particularly to fossil resources, which are controlled largely by elites — groups who tend almost systematically to resist greater accountability to the wider population. Encouraging those who currently control these fuel resources to recognise the potential fallout from the energy transition will be difficult, but no less essential to avoid further breakdowns in the relationship between governments and citizens.

But looking at energy transitions solely in terms of the fossil fuels that need to be replaced for the good of the planet only tells part of the story, and a discouraging part at that. The productive capacity of hydrocarbons is to be superseded by a new set of technologies with very different characteristics – ones which offer encouraging scope for peacebuilding. And while peace initiatives that leverage this opportunity are still few in number, they could offer significant potential at the intersection of development and peacebuilding.

At both the global and national levels, renewable technologies have the potential to decentralise the energy supply. In essence, fossil fuels are concentrated energy sources – existing in deposits underground, they are available to whomever is fortunate enough to own the land or sea above them. As a result, their value as a trading commodity has endowed those who possess them with political and military power.

For example, the initial international responses to Russia's invasion of Ukraine were gravely undermined by Europe's dependence on Russian oil and gas – a dependence which, early in the war, was estimated to contribute US$800 million per day to Putin's war economy. More punitive measures against Russia were avoided for fear of being cut off from energy supplies, an omission which likely prolonged the conflict. Elsewhere, in both Iraq and Lebanon, political elites, warlords and militias have been able to use their control of these energy sources for profiteering, rewarding allies and undermining rivals.[205]

Renewable energies can help in avoiding this centralisation, monopoly and weaponisation of energy sources in future – while unlocking great potential for economic development. Both wind and solar sources are accessible to some degree in every country, while hydropower potential exists in most.[i] Solar energy is especially plentiful

---

i Where renewable energy sources are less abundant, electricity interconnectors can be used to transmit the power from one country to another. There are now plans to lay a subsea cable between Morocco and the UK. Energy produced from solar and wind will be channelled 3,800 km beneath the sea, but at the same time creating fears of a new form of energy dependence even in the renewable era.

across Africa and can be deployed at a small scale and relatively inexpensively, especially if the energy storage challenge can be solved.[i] Yet that continent accounts for a mere one per cent of the world's installed solar and wind capacity and four per cent of its hydropower.[206] The European Investment Bank has highlighted the potential for investing in many African countries' solar and wind power to produce green hydrogen, some of which could be exported to Europe, where there is a particular demand because of the war in Ukraine and the virtual end of Russian gas supplies. Assurances of export revenue would certainly make it easier to raise investment for such projects.

Investment into African renewables would serve many purposes. It would naturally be an important component to mitigation measures for carbon emissions, and the revenues would contribute to adaptation (making life more feasible and bearable for large sectors of the population) at the same time as reducing motivations both for migration and conflict. But as so often when dealing with the climate change and conflict nexus, there is a chicken-and-egg element to it. To reduce conflict and increase security you need investment, but to get investment you need a modicum of security. To give just two examples, jihadists have delayed energy projects in Mozambique and in Nigeria.

Nevertheless, as renewable energy technologies become more widely available, the geopolitical power directly afforded to countries in possession of fossil resources is likely to be spread more evenly and could mitigate their role in inter-state conflict.[207] The same applies to their potential contribution to peace at the domestic or intra-state level. They do this by providing additional energy access to areas excluded from national grids, by creating opportunities for maintaining

---

i Since renewable energy sources such as solar and wind vary in their availability throughout the day, storing the electricity in batteries is essential to maximise production and ensure a stable supply. In large-scale grid systems, battery banks are rarely large enough to store the excess energy produced and can be expensive. In smaller systems, however, where batteries are available and affordable, they can store the excess energy and provide power throughout night.

livelihoods in fragile areas, and by permitting more decentralised and local ownership of energy production.[i]

With assistance from the UN Support Office in Somalia (UNSOS), the city of Baidoa is set to make a major step in the direction of renewable energy. A contract was recently finalised between a private energy provider, Kube Energy, and UNSOS to provide 20 MW of solar power to the city. Most of the energy produced will be provided to the people of Baidoa (16 MW) and the rest will go towards powering the UN camp.[208] This new solar facility will seek to displace the reliance on private diesel-powered generators that are very common in the city, not only reducing the emissions from energy production, but also offering a cheaper source of energy to create and sustain livelihoods throughout its expected lifetime of 25 years.

This project can be seen as a positive development on two fronts. The first and most obvious is the environment. The transition of the city's energy sector from diesel and charcoal to solar power will reduce carbon emissions, while the harmful air pollution caused by individual diesel motor generation will likewise be minimised. The second impact is the project's contribution to peace. By providing a cheaper and more reliable source of energy, it is expected to benefit local business development and the creation of livelihoods, in addition to the jobs created at the plant itself. And with the transfer of ownership from the private company to Baidoa after 15 years, the project is likely to support economic development in the longer term, alleviating some of the socioeconomic pressures that make conflict more likely.

Mali is one example of an African military dictatorship installed by a recent coup that facilitates corruption of the energy and mining sectors and, ultimately, further conflict. Corruption frequently leads to the exclusion of communities which is often the underlying cause for

---

i However, it should be noted that when the production and deployment of renewable technologies are not conducted in a conflict sensitive way, this can increase the chances that they will be controlled exclusively by elites, who divert and corrupt revenues to maintain their own standing – a process known as 'elite capture'. Land required for wind turbines, solar farms and the water required for cooling can be seized by corporate actors at the expense of those with informal customary rights.

conflict. In addition, the siphoning of the proceeds of corruption can then be used to bankroll methods of authoritarian control as well as new military operations, sometimes with the aid of foreign mercenaries.

After two military coups in 2020 and 2021, the new leadership invited in the Wagner mercenary group. With Russian connivance, Bamako requested in 2023 the withdrawal by the end of the year of the UN's mission in Mali (MINUSMA), the largest and highest-casualty UN peacekeeping operation. The mission had been authorised by the Security Council to help the former civilian government deal with the threat from jihadist groups. Prior to its departure, the UN worked to bring renewable forms of power, in a country where the lack of access to energy had exacerbated the grievances central to the conflict.[209]

In the rural areas in the north of Mali, where less than two per cent of the population has access to electricity from the grid, diesel-powered generators are used to supply energy for basic needs. The 2015 peace agreement aimed to address that imbalance between the slightly richer South of the country and the more marginalised North, and recognised the need for further electrification of the North, although little has so far been achieved on this front. While that promise remains unfulfilled, the supply of diesel continues to be channelled through armed groups, who gain revenue and influence from its distribution. In Mali's capital Bamako, MINUSMA piloted a private sector finance scheme for solar energy deployment, complementing the World Bank's renewable energy initiatives there. This will be based on a combination of mini-grids, supplying energy to remote areas, and larger-scale plants, connecting all primary and secondary cities in Mali to electricity.[210]

As mentioned earlier, developers of large renewable energy plants are often deterred by the unstable conditions in countries such as Mali; contract enforcement is relatively difficult and regulation is weak. The successive military coups have provided little incentive for private sector investment. The project in Bamako sought to overcome this difficulty by using the UN as what is known as an 'anchor client' – a party which is guaranteed to create revenue in the longer term.

Beyond financial feasibility, the most significant aspect of MINUSMA's commitment to renewables was its role in generating peace dividends, despite the recent serious challenges that the mission faced with the government. First, by shoring up the energy market in Mali, it provided a reliable source of electricity to meet the beneficiaries' development needs by aiding livelihood creation. Secondly, it hindered the ability of armed groups in control of diesel supply chains to benefit from its provision. And lastly, by helping to fulfil the promises of electrification from the 2015 peace agreement, it sought to increase trust in the peace process and its ability to deliver for local communities.

The models developed in Somalia and Mali could well be replicated elsewhere, particularly in post-conflict contexts. With support for the development of off-grid electricity generation (or through mini-grids), communities will have more reliable and safe access to power. By bridging renewable energy technologies and peacebuilding, we may unlock "an underappreciated tool for limiting conflict and maintaining peaceful societies" as a recent Center for Strategic and International Studies (CSIS) report rightly points out.[211]

But realising its potential will also require changes in the way donors approach reconstruction in post-conflict areas. In 2014, Siemens – with support from international donors – won a contract to build a gas turbine in Baiji district in Iraq, which was subsequently destroyed by ISIS. In Lebanon in 2022, over US$100 million was provided for the construction of the Zahrani power station, which had been forced offline due to a lack of fuel. A similar case can be seen in Yemen with the Marib power plant.[212] Investing in such large-scale energy projects is often attractive to donors, as rehabilitating old power plants can be more effective, and some donor governments may also see benefit in introducing international energy companies (often from their own countries) into these settings. Unlike renewables, these projects generate greenhouse gas emissions, and they can also create a dependency on imported coal, fuel oil or fossil gas for decades to come. The hope is that donors will soon come to understand that these investments are risky, drive corruption and create a financial burden, and conclude, instead, that investing in numerous small-scale decentralised renewable systems will have a more tangible impact on the civilian population.

All in all, while evidently not anywhere near as great a threat to stability as climate change itself, it needs to be recognised that the responses to climate change (via the reduction of emissions) also have the potential to generate tensions in developed and developing countries alike. The various forms of energy transition that countries will have to undertake are going to have to be managed with extreme care to mitigate their negative impacts and thus reduce the likelihood of new conflict. Conversely, some steps in the transition away from fossil fuels could also serve as a means to bring parties in conflict towards a more peaceful approach to one another. The energy transition, which is still barely under way, and how it plays out in different places, is a critical but relatively unexplored factor in the relationship between climate change and conflict.

6 Adaptation in conflict areas

It is now increasingly evident that there is little prospect of keeping global warming within the 1.5°C 'guardrail' that has been the stated goal of each COP summit.[213] The extreme weather events that threaten the safety and wellbeing of populations in conflict-affected areas will continue to increase for the foreseeable future.

The role of climate change in conflict is far from straightforward, with many aspects of it the subject of intense debate. But as noted in previous chapters, both the changes directly caused by climate change and those that result from our efforts to deal with it can aggravate existing tensions and flashpoints. What is needed to address these points of insecurity is adaptation, defined in climate policy as "the process of adjustment to actual or expected climate and its effects".[214] This involves changing processes, practices and structures to moderate potential damage or leverage opportunities associated with climate change. It is not just about attempting to mitigate emissions and reverse our impact on the climate. It is about changing the decisions we make to minimise the risks that climate change poses.

The composite nature of these risks — both environmental and social — is increasingly recognised, and is reflected in one of the foremost measures of climate vulnerability. Developed by the Notre Dame Global Adaptation Initiative, the ND- GAIN index uses the last 17 years of data to measure vulnerability and adaptive capacity. It looks at the physical implications of a changing climate, overlain onto social factors in each country. It recognises that high levels of social inequality and weak rule of law can undermine a state's ability to adapt to climate change.

Sufficient adaptive capacity is critical if society is to respond adequately to the risks posed by climate change. Environmental adaptation — such as building sea walls, growing drought-resistant crops and planting trees to absorb urban heat — helps to safeguard livelihoods in vulnerable regions and thus contributes to human security. But creating resilient societies that can mount an effective response to emerging conflicts — through democratisation or mediation support, for instance — is just as important.

Designing, implementing and financing appropriate adaptation strategies is a complicated process, hard enough even in countries that have relative stability. But for adaptation measures in conflict-affected areas, it can seem almost impossible. There are two obvious reasons for this. A state that has recently been afflicted by conflict and instability within its territory is rarely considered by donors, banks and businesses to be a promising recipient of climate finance. And even when funds may be made available, conditions on the ground can make the actual implementation of adaptation measures yet more challenging.

We should examine both of these factors separately. First, there is the climate financing gap. Despite promises made at COP15 in Copenhagen in 2009 and their renewal at subsequent meetings, the target of US$100 billion per year by 2020 has still not been met (in late 2023). This lack of climate finance is particularly apparent in conflict-affected countries. Even if more funding is made available by the wealthier countries, it is rarely directed towards fragile and conflict-affected areas.

On the contrary, climate financing seems particularly risk-averse.[215] It seeks — understandably enough — a stable lending environment where the likelihood of a project reaching completion is high. This is one of the reasons why the Israeli military authorities repeatedly confiscate or destroy solar power and water installations funded by European countries and the EU in the Palestinian territories on the West Bank; such actions are intended to discourage further investment and development projects by donors, because 'de-development' (leading to 'voluntary' emigration) is part of the goal.[216] Similarly, Russian policy in Ukraine since the 2022 invasion is designed in part to make the country appear as unattractive as possible to investors and businesses.

Countries that are both affected by conflict and also vulnerable to climate change by definition do not make for a favourable lending environment in a commercial sense. Most of the large green private sector investors in the world can only accept 'investment grade' risk, and seek a commercial return balanced against that higher risk that is hard to achieve in poorer economies that have a weak credit rating. And when you move away from mitigation projects to adaptation projects, the chance of drawing in the private sector diminishes even further. This is because many adaptation measures involve high capital costs (such as building sea walls or infrastructure that is resilient to natural disaster) but do not generate any income that might tempt investors, in contrast to some mitigation projects (such as turbines for wind power) that can lead to serious returns on investment. But adding conflict to investors' concerns, it becomes near impossible to scale up climate adaptation finance in these countries.

Of the US$14 billion disbursed by UN climate funds, fragile developing states received only one eightieth of the funding per capita compared to the amount received by non-fragile developing countries.[217] Between 2014 and 2021, only one country (DRC) ranked as 'extremely fragile' was among the top 15 recipients of climate finance.[218] This lack of support for areas that are most vulnerable to both climate change and conflict is a fairly clear-cut abdication of the responsibility to 'leave no one behind', as set out in the UN's 2030 Agenda, and a fundamental challenge to building climate resilience in the areas that are most at risk.

The second reason relates to implementation. When financial support is issued to fragile areas, it is not always easy to ensure that adaptation programmes adhere to the 'do no harm' principle, let alone that they additionally support peacebuilding. Adaptation can alter the political economy of the target area. In areas with a history of violent conflict, adaptive measures may aggravate conflict over resources, affecting their allocation and the surrounding power dynamics.[219] During the 'Green Revolution' of the 1970s, some of the measures implemented had unintended negative impacts, including environmental degradation and biodiversity loss, and heightened social tensions. In some countries, the benefits accrued to wealthier farmers and the cronies of military dictators, rather than to those most in need. It has thus been argued that although the Green Revolution increased food production, it also worsened conflict in countries from Sierra Leone to the Philippines.[220]

Avoiding such climate adaptation risks requires a more conflict-sensitive approach than has been adopted in the past. Before analysing ways to achieve this, it may be instructive to look at one specific case where this programming failed – where efforts to mitigate climate risk had the effect of actually catalysing conflict, a process known variously as 'maladaptation' or 'backdraft'.[221]

In Afghanistan, the mean annual temperature is increasing at one and a half times the global average, with a rise of 1.8°C since 1950,[222] making Afghanistan one of the world's ten countries most vulnerable to climate change.[223] With droughts becoming longer and harsher, the demand for water for agriculture, particularly in summer, is immense. In an attempt to support adaptation to the changing climate and provide increased water security for local farmers, the construction of the Salma Dam began in 2006. The project was finally completed in 2016 with the support of the Indian government (and was subsequently renamed the 'Afghan-India Friendship Dam').[224] After its construction, the dam was meant to increase the water supply to 42,000 hectares of land, with a further area of similar size provided with irrigation for the first time.[i]

---

i The dam is not just an adaptation project, but also, as pointed out by Krampe, Hegazi and VanDeveer, a development and climate change mitigation project.[225] It provides extended access to electricity in Herat Province, and on mitigation, it reduces the greenhouse gas emissions from electricity production and was rightly included in Afghanistan's NDC to the UNFCCC. However, it also demonstrates many of the challenges associated with climate adaptation projects, especially those with a large impact.

Notwithstanding the intensive conflict resulting from the Taliban insurgency and the international community's failed attempt to prevent it, most violent disputes in Afghanistan tend to arise from disagreements over land and water.[226] The Salma Dam is a case in point. Decision-making on the distribution of water from the completed dam were taken at the state level and apparently paid little heed to dynamics among the communities around the dam itself.[227] After the dam's completion, some areas suffered from water scarcity as a result of the redistribution of water resources, which many of the intended beneficiaries, particularly local farmers, perceived as unfair. As a result, there was a rise in levels of conflict. In one downstream village, Shakiban in the Zinda Jan district, locals attempted to build a diversion weir to reclaim some of the water flow lost as a result of the dam's construction. Inevitably, this action deprived some of the villagers' downstream neighbours of their now plentiful supply. When some of these communities tried to contest the decision, 600 armed men from Shakiban gathered at the weir and violence erupted.[228] [i]

As we saw in Chapter 5 on the energy transition, it is not just climate change itself that can make conflict situations worse. Adaptation and development projects that are designed in response to climate change also have the clear potential to exacerbate existing conflicts and even provoke new ones. As the need for adaptation grows in fragile and conflict-affected areas, interventions to build adaptive capacity cannot afford to overlook political and social contexts. Greater cooperation between peacebuilding and development actors is therefore required. The integration of comprehensive conflict analyses into climate and development projects would buttress the 'do no harm' principle and also highlight the opportunities to improve social justice, beyond simply reducing violence.

---

i This was not the first time that the construction of a dam in Afghanistan had unfortunate consequences for peace and stability. As part of its Cold War policy to keep Afghanistan in the camp of the 'free world', the US provided loans for dams across the Helmand River, including the Kajaki Dam. The financial costs were huge, local farmers were taxed to pay for some of them, it led to salination of some of the irrigated land, thereby reducing crop yields, did not generate much power, and by the 1970s accounted for a massive 20 per cent of Afghanistan's national budget. The Soviet Union responded by offering loans for other costly dam projects, which were also not very successful. The whole dam saga contributed to a loss of credibility for the King and his Prime Minister, and therefore the revolution that overthrew them, and ultimately the Soviet invasion that led to nearly half a century of conflict.[229]

The Great Green Wall (GGW) Initiative, which can lay claim to being the largest and most audacious environmental undertaking in history, is currently under way across the breadth of the Sahel. First conceived in the 1970s but launched in 2007, it aims to combat the desertification that is continuously extending southward from the Sahara. The goal is to regenerate an area of land 8,000 km long from Senegal on the Atlantic all the way to Djibouti on the Red Sea.[i] In the vast expanse of the Sahel, where 80 per cent of the land has been degraded by a combination of over-grazing and climate change, most inhabitants are employed in agriculture. The ongoing desertification therefore threatens livelihoods as well as the local environment. Desertification, underway for many decades, is now accelerating as a result of global warming, and adaptation is an urgent necessity.

Due to its gargantuan scale and ambition, the project has attracted much attention, both positive and negative, from the international community. The debate demonstrates some of the challenges of adaptation in fragile contexts, but its relative success to date also offers glimpses of ways forward.

Since independence in the 1960s, the countries that make up the Sahel have experienced numerous inter-ethnic, intra-state conflicts. Conflict continues to plague a number of Sahelian states – Mali and Sudan have suffered particularly in this regard. Partly because of these challenging conditions, governments have shown understandable enthusiasm for the Great Green Wall. The official GGW 2020 report notes that a shared realisation of the severity of the climate challenge includes the recognition that these challenges must be tackled collectively if the solutions are to be effective.[230] The African Union and its numerous partner organisations (including the UN, EU and World Bank) have committed to supporting the 20 member states participating in the programme.

---

i Desertification is not uniquely a product of climate change; it is also caused by other aggravating factors such as extractive land management practices. However, the risks from desertification are predicted to increase due to climate change, reducing biodiversity and the productivity of land and livestock, according to the IPCC *Special Report on Climate Change and Land*.

Various governments have demonstrated their willingness to address the threat of desertification in the Sahel region. While this is a positive development – buy- in at the level of the state being key to improving affected ecosystems – it only tells part of the story. As stated earlier, climate change impacts are felt most keenly at the local level. There has been, at least until now, no instance of inter-state armed conflict arising directly and primarily from climate-related challenges; it is usually at the intra-state and community levels where climate change is a conflict risk factor.

So while commitment from governments is a necessary step in the right direction, it alone cannot provide for an effective programme to reduce climate risk, particularly given the heterogeneous ethnic and cultural make-up of the affected states. If initiatives are taken up solely by state institutions, they may aggravate already tense social and political dynamics, as seen with the Salma Dam. Instead, for a successful outcome, locally tailored programmes which respect cultural, ecological and political diversity across the Sahel region are required.

In its early form, the GGW was not designed to be such a programme. Its original mission was to reforest a belt 16 km wide across the Sahel region. It saw the solution to the desertification from the Sahara as lying in wide-scale planting of trees, maintaining soil integrity and providing nutrients for other plants. However, many of the trees were planted in unsuitable locations;[231] [i] large numbers of saplings then withered and died, either because they were unsuited to the harsh environment or because there was no one to tend and water them. The strong top-down approach ignored the local sensitivities that must be considered for such a programme to work. It also lent itself to corruption, particularly in areas with weak governance. In retrospect, the one-size-fits-all policy was doomed from the start, and even now, much of the criticism of the GGW seems to stem from perceptions of that initial approach.

---

i This strategy has also been applied to combat the southward movement of the Gobi Desert into Inner Mongolia in China, encountering similar issues. Initiated in 1978, the Three-North Shelter Forest Programme (TNSP) has run into difficulty with diseases and land erosion, caused by planting saplings in areas unviable for growth, and by monoculture afforestation.[232] In one case in Ningxia in 2000, the vulnerability caused by monoculture afforestation saw a disease eliminate one billion trees – two decades' worth of planting.[233]

Now with a fresh approach, the initiative has mutated into a "mosaic of land use practices"[234] which involves implementing agricultural and ecological projects and making use of local and indigenous systems of land management. The GGW has become a movement aimed at regenerating land, spanning a much broader area and range of practices than the green belt first envisioned. In Ethiopia, the GGW has supplied five billion plants and seeds to communities, supported windbreaks (shrubs and vegetation to stall the expanding desertification),[i] restored almost 800,000 hectares of terraces, and trained over 60,000 people in food and energy security.[235]

In Eritrea, GGW activities have focused on soil and water conservation. Almost 130 million saplings have been planted and farmland has been terraced to increase water retention for agriculture. In Senegal, 12 million drought-resistant trees have been planted in a bid to boost agro-forestry initiatives in selected areas of the country. Most of the trees planted in Senegal are *Acacia senegal*, a variety of acacia which can survive long periods of drought while providing shelter and fodder for animals, and which should be of interest to peacebuilders. Its advantages are particularly apparent in the context of the GGW: 40 per cent of the tree's mass lies in its roots, whose underground sprawl improves soil integrity and, importantly, fixes nitrogen, reducing the need for synthetic fertilisers. When planted in grids of 10 m^2, it can be used in an intercropping system with millet, sorghum or beans, which are more likely to flourish thanks to the supply of water and organic matter stored in the earth by the root system. This technique has already been used to good effect in Niger and Senegal.[236]

Planting these trees offers another significant benefit. As well as providing shade, fodder and firewood, the trees produce resin, which can be collected during the dry season and sold commercially. Gum arabic, as it is known, is increasingly sought after by multinational companies due to its beneficial properties as an emulsifier and stabiliser in the food industry and its multiple uses in industrial products. In

---

i Not only do these windbreaks slow desertification, but they also provide shade, increasing the humidity of soil and improving the prospects for regeneration.

recent years, growing demand has seen the price of gum arabic increase by 158 per cent. Due to the unrest across the Sahel, attempts have been made to grow it elsewhere (in Texas, the Arabian Peninsula and South Asia, for example), but thus far, it has not been possible to replicate the quality of the product from the Sahel.[237] Farmers who master the technique will reap the benefits by increasing their agricultural productivity and generating revenue from selling gum arabic. A limited focus solely on planting trees is sure to fail, as was proved decades ago, but there should continue to be a role for species such as acacia. These trees offer additional livelihood security which supports adaptation to a challenging climate, enabling farmers to remain on land that would otherwise be swallowed up by the advancing desert and mitigating the violence that is so often the outcome of economic insecurity.

Perhaps the clearest departure from the initial GGW concept has taken place in Burkina Faso. As well as planting trees, GGW has supported the regeneration of three million hectares of land, using a local farming technology called *Zaï* to boost fertility and improve water infiltration. It involves digging holes, 10-20 cm deep, across a grid. The holes are then filled with manure, attracting termites, which play a crucial role in improving soil structure.[238] When undertaken at scale, this local technology can increase soil fertility and agricultural yields, mitigating food and livelihood insecurity.

Across the vast project area, GGW has created over 350,000 jobs and regenerated 18 million hectares of degraded land, with co-benefits for 15 of the 17 Sustainable Development Goals (SDGs). The programme helps to counteract the soil degradation caused by climate change and desertification and thus supports sustainable employment. The recruitment strategies of armed groups, identified earlier as a link between climate change and conflict, are less likely to be successful, while local communities can maintain their livelihoods in these regions.

GGW activities have also improved water security, reducing the burden on women, as well as their exposure to gender-based violence. Moreover, by improving prospects for local communities, GGW lessens the pressure to migrate and thus reduces tensions caused by urbanisation. Challenges may remain,[i] but the GGW's evolution from a uniform top-down initiative to a patchwork of localised solutions has demonstrated the necessity of the latter approach to adaptation. Since this change of direction, the Great Green Wall initiative has become far more successful, even inspiring governments in India and Saudi Arabia to implement their own green wall initiatives. And while it is the scale of it that makes the GGW so remarkable, elsewhere there have been some nationally driven initiatives that also shed light on how adaptive solutions can be tailored to local contexts.

Between 1996 and 2006, Nepal experienced a brutal civil war. A Maoist insurgency challenged the constitutional monarchy, drawing on the accumulation of ethnic, political and social grievances. Despite a new constitution and a series of successful elections, these divisions have yet to be comprehensively addressed.[240] Any development or adaptation interventions must therefore pay heed to these divisions and must ensure that external initiatives adhere to the 'do no harm' principle.

The political situation is not the only cause of instability in Nepal, however. The effects of climate change are increasingly felt across the country. Monsoon seasons have been changing, while droughts are becoming more common during the dry season.[241] Above all, there are the Himalayas. Named for the Nepalese word himal, meaning 'snow-covered mountain', this range contains the largest reserve of freshwater outside the two polar regions.[242] But with global heating, the glaciers holding this water are melting, releasing an estimated 174 trillion litres between 2003 and 2009.[243] This process, known as deglaciation, poses serious risks to downstream communities, as the floods that devastated Pakistan in the summer of 2022 made all too clear.

---

i While the scope and ambition of this initiative are truly impressive and fully commensurate with what is required, it is fair to say that these challenges are inevitably almost on the same scale. Particularly on the matter of funding, much of the money promised has yet to arrive – including most of the US$14 billion announced at the One Planet Summit co-hosted in 2021 by France, UN and the World Bank. In addition to the many adaptation benefits for the Sahel regions concerned (ranging from increasing food security and biodiversity to reducing terrorism and migration), there is an important climate mitigation component to it, given that once completed, the GGW could sequester up to 250 million tonnes of carbon dioxide each year.[239]

The village of Halji in Humla district is home to around 400 people, and the site of one of the oldest monasteries in Nepal. But each June between 2006 and 2011, the village experienced flash floods, which poured down from a glacier 1,700 m above, washing away fertile land, livestock and houses. Some of the poorest members of the community lost all their agricultural land, and with it their livelihoods.[244]

This combination of droughts, increased rainfall and shifting glaciers has driven people to migrate within Nepal and into neighbouring India. Expatriate remittances to Nepal have helped to boost local economies, but also pushed up land prices – another factor driving the socioeconomic inequality that played a key role in the earlier civil war.[245] Even without the effects of migration, marginalised groups are more at risk from the impacts of climate change. They generally live in less desirable areas, such as floodplains. As the wet seasons become wetter and more water is discharged from the glaciers, marginalised groups will suffer the most. This situation creates a risk of renewed violence – especially in a country where the recent conflict was fuelled by the grievances of the most marginalised groups in the first place.

Discussions on how Nepal should adapt to climate change started relatively early. The process of documenting Nepal's urgent adaptation needs began back in 2004.[246] Reports commissioned from international organisations and consultants noted the risks that climate change posed to development in Nepal and set out priority areas for adaptation, such as forestry and biodiversity, disaster management, water and urban energy.[247] However, given the periodically tumultuous state of politics in the years up until 2010, little progress was made. Conversations at the national level focused on the National Adaptation Plan of Action (NAPA), which was finalised in 2010 after an 18-month process, by which point it had become partly obsolete. The technical solutions that it proposed for the priority areas paid little attention either to the tense political reality in which the programme was to be implemented, or to the inequalities in political influence, caste, gender and ethnicity that added to Nepal's climate vulnerability.[248]

An alternative mechanism to support adaptation was also being formulated in the Local Adaptation Plans of Action (LAPAs), backed by the London-based peacebuilding NGO Saferworld.[249] The aim of these programmes was to ensure that adaptation measures could be implemented without risking further conflict in Nepal. Rather than viewing adaptation as a matter for the national level, this approach focused on the different districts and localities in Nepal. The pilot phase involved four districts, where stakeholders were identified within community-based organisations and local authorities. Shared learning workshops and a set of participatory analyses were conducted with these groups. This made it possible to assess the locally perceived climate-conflict dynamics, as well as the knock-on effect of potential adaptation measures on peace.[250] [i]

The LAPAs have since been implemented across Nepal, yet have retained their focus on community action and continued to engage those affected by measures in their design.[252] The programmes are now coordinated with both provincial and federal governments, which use their combined influence to implement comprehensive adaptation measures. Various types of initiatives have been supported. In some areas of Nepal, new irrigation pipes have been laid to support cardamom production, compensating for the reduced rainfall and snowfall in winter months. Elsewhere, a tea plantation has been set up in the expectation that the warmer weather will create the right conditions for a successful tea industry. And to replace some of the livelihoods lost in traditional agriculture, one project involved planting a shrub known as *lokta* to supply the raw material for paper production and support local industry.[253]

The aim of the LAPAs in Nepal was to empower beneficiaries of adaptation to influence its design. Financing from official development assistance (ODA) or from mechanisms such as the Green Climate Fund can trickle down and be used in ways that are appropriate to

---

i The focus on communities' perceptions here should be noted. In cases where natural resources become the subject of conflict, their mere redistribution is not a silver bullet for its resolution – how it is perceived and communicated is just as important. Even in a case where issues of genuine scarcity are addressed, disputes may linger on if one group sees its own access as inferior or inequitable relative to another's.[251]

local settings. With the involvement of marginalised groups, including women and children, in decision-making, it is possible to facilitate development activities that are conflict-sensitive.

However, there are still significant difficulties in amplifying the voices of the most vulnerable.[254] In research conducted in 2017, one study found that excluding vulnerable communities from adaptation planning exacerbated existing inequalities and exposure to climate hazards.[255] The main beneficiaries of improved irrigation systems in some parts of Nepal were often those who already possessed significant private wealth, while landless families were largely overlooked in the consultation exercises. For those struggling to make ends meet in an impoverished rural economy, migrating to an urban centre appears to offer attractive prospects, but this places additional burdens on institutions, communities, environments and resources; the incentives to engage in violence and civil unrest also increase. Adaptation programmes should aim to balance the need for high-level political support and resources through top-down approaches and generate buy-in and effectiveness through a locally tailored approach.

Adaptation strategies aim to create resilience to the impacts of climate change. This can be achieved in a multitude of ways, with the best methods differing according to where they are trialled. It may involve growing crops that are more resilient to changing seasonal patterns, or creating sea walls to protect against sea-level rise. But focusing exclusively on the physical impacts of climate change risks overlooking important social dimensions. Social factors are crucial in determining the extent to which climate change may foster human insecurity and conflict. Poor governance, gender divisions and armed groups all exist independently of climate change and create vulnerability.

Action to counter each of these challenges offers an entry point to address climate risks. By building their resilience to climate change, societies will also be better placed to respond in a peaceful manner to the other risks associated with a changing climate. In this context, environmental peacebuilding can be a significant tool in support of adaptation.

7 Environmental peacebuilding

This study has so far focused on the role of climate change in exacerbating conflict. But the relationship is not entirely one-way: conflict also has major impacts on the environment and biodiversity. It is now possible to detect some momentum building up for the use of the environment as a tool for consolidating peace. This is very recent, however. For over two millennia (and probably more), the environment has been used as a means to consolidate military gains.

In 146 BCE, during the Third Punic War, the Romans won a crushing victory over their Mediterranean rivals, the Carthaginians. For decades, they had been at war over trading routes between Sicily and Italy, with the Romans imposing increasingly punitive terms of surrender. As the war drew to its conclusion, the city of Carthage was sacked and burned over six days and 50,000 of its inhabitants were sold into slavery. According to one retelling, consul Scipio Aemilianus and his men took to the fields surrounding Carthage, sowing them not with seed, but with salt to ensure that the land could not be used to grow crops if the Carthaginians ever returned.

Although now thought to be apocryphal, the story illustrates how groups of people have periodically tried to manipulate nature to gain the upper hand over others. There are examples from British history as well: in 1069–70, soon after the Conquest, the Normans put down a revolt in northern England by destroying crops and causing mass starvation. Cromwell's army applied similar tactics in Ireland in the 1650s. In more recent times, we can look to the US war in Vietnam. As well as using the herbicide Agent Orange,[i] the US had another military tactic to modify the natural environment. From 1967 until 1972, Operation Popeye saw US planes fly from their bases in Thailand over North Vietnam on 'cloud seeding' missions. By releasing iodine from the planes into the clouds, they hoped to extend the monsoon season in the North, softening roads, causing landslides, and eventually cutting off military supply lines from North Vietnam and Laos. Several observers were appalled by this tactic. Senator Claiborne Pell, who chaired the 1972 hearings on the topic, declared, "If we do not restrict the military use of current environmental modification techniques, we risk the danger of the development of vastly more dangerous techniques whose consequences may be unknown or may cause irreparable damage to our global environment."[257] [ii]

Another example of terrible environmental destruction in conflict was Saddam Hussein's torching of the oil wells in Kuwait during the withdrawal of Iraqi forces in 1991. The worst cases of deliberate environmental destruction seem to have occurred in the context of inter-state wars. However, one especially grim example of intra-state eco-warfare was the damming and draining of the marshes of southern Iraq to force the Marsh Arabs, who the Iraqi leader accused of treachery during the 1980s war with Iran, from their homelands. This was carried out as an act of severe internal repression with overtones of cultural genocide.

---

i In the US, there was a considerable domestic backlash against the wide-scale use of defoliants, including Agent Orange (from 1961 until it was banned in 1971), to prevent the jungle being used as cover by the Viet Cong. Indeed, it has been argued that, alongside the publication of Rachel Carson's *Silent Spring* in 1962, it drove the fear that technology could lead to ecocide and therefore contributed to the creation of the modern environmentalist movement.[256]

ii This hearing led to the renunciation of environmental modification techniques in July 1972. In December 1976, the Convention on the Prohibition of Military or any other Hostile Use of Environmental Modification Techniques was approved by the UN General Assembly.

The invasion of Ukraine has also seen the use of the environment as both an offensive (by Russian forces) and defensive (by Ukraine) tactic, most notably with the deliberate use of flooding from reservoirs (see Chapter 8 for more).

Even when the environment is not being used for military purposes, the idea that ecological changes have the potential to exacerbate conflict pervades the political discourse, as we have seen. The question of how the environment can be engaged for peace remains, however. After all, not every diminishing resource gets fought over as a first course of action; and there are times when a desire for cooperation will trump competition and conflict. Finding ways to make cooperation the more likely outcome and to use the environment for peaceful ends, therefore, offers a potential strategy to alleviate the risk of climate-related conflict. It can also help build resilience to climate change in conflict-affected societies.

The practice of environmental peacebuilding builds on this idea, and looks to "stand the core premise of ecological (in)security on its head".[258] In their 2002 study, Conca and Dabelko set out to establish how environmental issues can help to enable peace, as opposed to triggering violent conflict, and to change the narrative of the climate-conflict nexus to one of climate and peace.[i] More recently, the framework of environmental peacebuilding has been increasingly adopted in discussions of the climate-conflict nexus.

The thinking behind it is relatively simple. Where there are conflicting parties, it can and should be possible to use the natural environment as an entry point for cooperation between them. The outcome of this cooperation, so the logic goes, will be a renewed degree of trust and ability to confront contentious issues, with benefits for the environment. In practice, this can take several forms, and can be loosely defined as "the multiple approaches and pathways by which the management of environmental issues is integrated in and can support conflict prevention,

---

i This shift can be seen as an attempt to soften the more catastrophic predictions of Kaplan and Homer- Dixon a few years earlier.[259]

mitigation, resolution and recovery".[260] This section will outline some aspects of this practice and offer examples that may increase its effectiveness for building peace in the face of the climate challenge.

As this is a relatively new approach to peacebuilding, much of the discussion has taken place in academic circles, relying on a limited number of practical case studies being available for review. Its early development saw an exclusive focus on inter-state cooperation, but in the last 20 years, scholars and practitioners have built on this framework with more detail and have begun to implement it in the context of intra-state conflicts, following the recent trends in violent conflict.[261]

Environmental peacebuilding is in theory applicable at any level: geopolitical, inter-state, national and local. US Climate Envoy John Kerry's visit to China is a potential example: it took place in July 2023, when tensions between the two superpowers (and the world's two highest emitters) were running high. As he arrived, Kerry said: "We are very hopeful that this can be the beginning not just of a conversation ... on the climate track, but that we can begin to change the broader relationship." Prior to that, Washington had hoped to keep the climate discussions going regardless of the state of its overall relationship with Beijing, although the latter had different views: as one analyst put it, "for the Chinese, geopolitics is the tail that wags the climate dog, not the reverse."[262]

However, environmental peacebuilding has more often taken a local and community-based approach. One of the most prominent and often-cited examples of environmental peacebuilding is the Good Water Neighbours (GWN) project, undertaken by EcoPeace Middle East in 2001. In many regions in the Middle East, water scarcity has exacerbated the long-standing political conflicts both within and between states.[263] From the perspective of environmental peacebuilding, it therefore offers an entry point for cooperation and easing of historical tensions. EcoPeace Middle East implemented the GWN project on the borders between Jordan, Palestine and Israel, looking to engage cross-border communities and use "their mutual dependence on shared water resources as a basis for cooperation".[264]

The project connected 28 cross-border communities that share the Jordan River: eleven from Palestine, nine from Israel, and eight from Jordan. It supported visits between these communities and advocated for the introduction of ecological training within the education curriculum. The final report on the programme concluded: "the direct interaction broke down the stereotypical image of an enemy, creating the basic foundations for lasting peace through individual friendships."[265] After three years of project activities, 86 per cent of people involved said that they understood the need to work together to protect their shared water resources, and 78 per cent of participants demonstrated a more positive attitude towards their cross-boundary neighbours. After years of fractious relations and mutual blaming for the decline in the Jordan River flow, the GWN project went some way towards improving these relationships.[266] As a result of the programme, a sewage network was set up to transfer wastewater from the Palestinian community to a treatment site in Israel, and a model farm was established in South Ghore, Jordan, in cooperation with Israeli farmers in order to boost productivity and solve agricultural issues. To support these cross-border initiatives, EcoPeace has helped raise over half a billion US dollars – a feat made possible by its long-standing engagement combined with its impressive advocacy at the political level.[267]

Local government officials can be effective actors in transboundary environmental peacebuilding, even when national governments are reluctant to engage in cooperation or discussion. Municipal actors were a useful entry point for cooperation in the GWN project. Through a network of mayors and decision-makers along the border area, they managed to petition Israel to double its allocation of water to Gaza and to supply the West Bank city of Rawabi. Local leaders can thus lay a foundation for environmental peacebuilding when national governments are not ready.

We can also see this in action at the higher political level in the Jordan-Israel-UAE Water-for-Energy Deal, originally planned to include Palestine. Environmental conditions in these partner countries differ considerably (desert, coastline, mountains, high winds), enabling them to build on each other's strengths to reduce greenhouse gas emissions, perhaps by importing solar, hydrogen or wind power and exporting desalinated or underground water to more water-scarce nations.[268] Clearly, energy and water agreements based on the concept of interdependence could offer a great opportunity for the Middle East to advance regional economic integration and boost regional stability by increasing the costs of conflict for both sides. The fact that environmental peacebuilding has not succeeded in bringing this about cannot be blamed on the concept itself. If the stronger party to a conflict is explicit about not wanting to negotiate any sort of acceptable peace with the other side, then no amount of well-intentioned, cleverly- designed environmental peacebuilding is likely to succeed.

In conflicts where the two main adversaries do have some desire to progress towards peace, even nominally, the effects of transboundary cooperation may be felt by local communities, enabling them to experience the benefits of improved relations with the other group. Tangible benefits (improved water quality and flow, cheaper energy in the case of water-for-energy trade) can help to promote positive peace even beyond the affected communities. However, combining these two aspects (peacebuilding and environment) also poses some risks of its own, as explained by Tobias Ide, one of the most influential academic voices in this field.[269]

According to Ide, one of the biggest risks is 'de-politicisation' (normally considered a virtue, but not in this instance). This occurs when environmental issues are viewed as being disconnected from political and social issues. Particularly in areas where resources are scarce or the source of competition, it may be a mistake to assume that the environment is not a political issue. A focus on technical or scientific (as opposed to political) solutions can make it more challenging to address underlying drivers of insecurity and conflict.[270]

Ide gives an example from Pakistan in 2010, when serious flooding struck areas along the Indus River. The international community and local NGOs provided financial and technical support for future disaster risk reduction, including improved building materials and advice on safer construction practices. Together, they were able to accelerate the process of reconstruction in the wake of the disaster. However, it was not only poor building practices (similar to Rousseau's accurate observation about Lisbon in 1756, cited in Chapter 3) that had paved the way for what happened in Pakistan. Clientelism, high wealth inequality and weak state presence had undermined the communities' capacity to handle the disaster. And yet the response focused mainly on the 'hard' material problems and failed to seize the opportunity to address the social and political drivers of vulnerability.[271]

Vulnerability, as noted before, can be created by the poor functioning or, indeed, the absence of social structures. Integrating conflict issues into strategies for environmental peacebuilding is therefore essential, whereas failure to do so can limit and even reverse any knock-on effects that support peacebuilding. An example of this was seen in Cyprus.

In Cyprus, where annual rainfall is predicted to decrease by 10–15 per cent by 2050,[272] water has long been a challenge to livelihoods and peace. Since the inter-communal violence that led to the Greek-ordered coup and then the Turkish invasion in 1974, the island has been divided, with no integrated water management system operating between the two territories. The ecosystems that both Turkish and Greek Cypriot communities share are still subject to the divisions that the conflict arbitrarily produced. And while environmental issues have been addressed on both sides of the divide, the failure to cooperate in managing them has impeded the prospects for a sustainable solution.

Recognising this, UNDP attempted to engage in a form of environmental peacebuilding by involving the two communities in joint initiatives such as reforestation and waste management. In 2005, they set up Action for Cooperation and Trust (ACT) to support reconciliation efforts. Based on the idea that nature knows no boundaries, the project engaged in a number of environmental initiatives: organic farming, biodiversity conservation in the buffer zone, and joint management of artificial wetlands. The cooperation was formalised in 2007 in the Cyprus Environmental Stakeholder Forum, connecting organisations responsible for documenting shared environmental problems. Through this forum, ACT initiated two main projects. The first involved the development of a database of environmental stakeholders, a list of funding opportunities for interested NGOs, and information on environmental education opportunities. The second was a research project on biodiversity in the buffer zone, which documented its abundant flora and fauna, thereby "unearthing a new common environmental and ecological heritage for the island".[273]

A survey of the Greek and Turkish Cypriot NGOs which had participated in the programme concluded that trust had been built between the two communities.[274] The survey found tolerance and understanding strengthened on both sides, and showed that some participants were willing to think of the environment beyond their ethno-territorial identification.

Nonetheless, the assessment of the programme highlighted some limits to ACT's peacebuilding effects. The shared sense of environment that the project aimed to create was felt more strongly among Greek Cypriots than on the Turkish side – although perhaps this is not surprising given their claim that the division of the island, and therefore by definition any Turkish-controlled territory at all, is illegitimate. The mistrust between Greek and Turkish NGOs still characterised many responses, and it was suggested that where a feeling of greater togetherness had developed, it was between particular NGO members, rather than the broader community.[275]

The UNDP ACT project may have contributed to more sustainable ecosystems on Cyprus. It took a conventional environmental peacebuilding approach, implementing initiatives in the hope that cooperation would foster peaceful relations. But it is seen by some observers to have struggled owing to its lack of engagement with the ethno-political issues that had of course prompted the conflict in the first place. In this sense, the peacebuilding component was not fulfilled. Initiatives relied on the hope that the spillover effects of environmental cooperation would contribute to addressing long-standing grievances – a dependence that is a common, albeit understandable, pitfall of environmental peacebuilding programming.[i] Integrating cultural,

---

i De-politicisation' being one of the six Ds that make up what Ide calls the 'dark side' of environmental peacebuilding.[276]

economic and political factors into the programming is an important step in enabling environmental peacebuilding to transform the way in which groups relate to the environment and each other.

After the Second Congo War ended in 2003, the Eastern DRC was held together by a fragile peace agreement.[277] South Kivu, which had suffered grievously from years of conflict, was also struggling on another front: poor water management had led to an outbreak of cholera in the community. In many areas, the water sources were divided between villages, and in one case, disagreement over distribution issues came close to escalating into open conflict.[278] The seeds for its resolution, however, had been sown several years earlier. In 2003, the UK-based aid agency Tearfund begun consultations with communities in Swima Village, and agreed to support capacity-building in water management through the establishment of a Committee for Clean Water, in which women would be represented by quota. After all, women were the experts here, having learnt about water-borne diseases from their time in refugee camps in Burundi and Tanzania during the war.[279]

Three years later, with the Committee well-established in the community, a long-standing conflict was reignited between Swima and its upstream neighbour Ihua Village. Envious of the new water system that their neighbours had managed to set up, members of the Ihua community proceeded to throw waste into the river, contaminating the water flowing to Swima. Building on the tensions left over from the war, they provocatively branded Swima people the "consumers of Ihua waste".[280] In 2007, when the prospect of open conflict again loomed, Swima women from the Committee put together a plan to re-design the water supply, sourcing it from rivers upstream of Ihua. Reaching out to the women in Ihua, the communities agreed to extend the reach of the water system to include both villages. Together, they built the infrastructure required for the extension, and through this process of interaction, encouraged reconciliation between the two communities.[281] The cooperation was widely regarded as a success, with the Committee registered with the government as an official partner in water provisioning services. Soon, it was providing safe water to over 60,000 people in the area.

Integrating the Women, Peace and Security (WPS) agenda into environmental peacebuilding is not only a means of responding to the specific impacts of climate change on women. It also opens the door for peacebuilders to harness the knowledge and experience that women in vulnerable societies possess.[i] South Kivu is one example of how women's inclusion in environmental peacebuilding can facilitate peaceful settlements which also lay the foundations for sustainable and equitable resource management.

As mentioned, environmental peacebuilding encompasses a wide range of activities. In the few examples discussed so far, we have seen efforts to support dialogue around natural resources, a database for environmental initiatives, a research project celebrating biodiversity, and institutional support for female representation. Each of these approaches addresses different needs and sensitivities. But one aspect — and a critical one — which has yet to be discussed is the importance of awareness-raising and education on climate change.

For successful environmental mediation, and as a foundation of sustainable adaptation measures, local awareness and understanding of the issues is essential. In areas where access to education remains limited, communities' ability to adapt to climate change continues to be held back. In many parts of Africa and South Asia, where climate change poses the most risk, levels of education are low — an issue aggravated by school closures during the Covid-19 pandemic. According to the World Bank, as many as 70 per cent of ten-year-olds in low- and middle-income countries cannot read a simple text, and only half of the population in Africa may have heard of climate change as a concept, even if they are all too aware of its consequences.[283] But even in the developed world, there is striking ignorance about climate issues. In August 2023, the Washington Post published a poll which showed that far more Americans misguidedly

i For a similar example, see the project in Yemen funded by the UN Peacebuilding Fund. This project has similarly harnessed women's role in water management in its peacebuilding strategy. Through assigned quotas for their inclusion in local water user associations and conflict resolution committees, women have been involved in negotiations and mediation around water usage. Being more inclusive of women and girls meant that "the project not only accrued benefits for women; women also contributed to larger water management improvement goals."[282]

believed that recycling their garbage would do more to combat climate change than eating less meat or reducing their air travel.[284]

Improved education – including on climate change – enables communities to re-think existing practices, and fosters their willingness to change. This is especially the case if climate awareness and human rights education are combined; a knowledge of universal rights is an essential condition for being able to defend or promote them, either on one's own or another's behalf. Looking at mortality rates after natural disasters in Nepal and their intersection with education, a recent study concluded that the most reliable predictor of survival post-disaster is education, greater even than wealth and income.[285] Key literacy skills enable people to read life-saving instructions, to inform themselves about disaster-resistant crops, and to learn about safe construction in areas where such disasters are predicted. All of these are the outcome of education, which can build the human capacities and financial resources required for adaptation. Simply giving people the skills for effective advocacy could significantly improve the long-term prospects of many people living in such areas.

Education on climate issues takes various forms. It includes technical knowledge, such as being aware of which species of tree or agro-forestry system is most suitable in a given area or which forms of irrigation or crop storage might be most effective. Educating communities to challenge traditional beliefs may, if handled sensitively, also produce results. For example, some families in West African communities familiar to the author (see Preface) were reluctant to use a solar cooker because they believed that food should be cooked over firewood to give it its typical smoky flavour. A sensitive approach may help to change mindsets and encourage climate-friendly behaviour in such contexts.

In Germany, the Berghof Foundation has been using *peace education* tools to empower young people in the face of climate change. In the digital peace education project "Our future?! Youth in dialogue about climate change and sustainable peace", there were moving moments when young people from different regions of the world shared their views on the challenges posed by climate change. The encounter focused on personal concerns and on the intra-societal and international dimensions of climate change. Reflections circled around the question of how to transform the destructive developments accompanying climate change in ways which would sustain rather than threaten peace.

Peace education can promote a commitment to climate action. This involves creating opportunities for dialogue and providing learning material for people from various world regions to discuss strategies and visions for dealing with climate change. The connections between climate change and violent conflict – and the historical responsibilities for it – must be made visible from different perspectives. Peer learning is important, and a valuable tool to explore this. By fostering their expertise through education programmes, individuals can learn to perceive themselves as agents of change or as role models who actively and self-confidently stand up against the effects of climate change and advocate for peaceful coexistence.

As in peacebuilding more generally, recognising the different ways in which men and women are affected is important in educational approaches. In one study on sub-Saharan Africa, researchers estimate that increasing the ratio of young women who have completed their education from 30 to 70 per cent could reduce the death toll from extreme weather events by 60 per cent.[286] The disproportionate impact of climate change on women can also be addressed through this type of initiative, or as Ugandan climate activist Vanessa Nakate puts it: "Education prepares girls to advocate for themselves and to tackle the social-justice issues at the heart of the climate crisis. When girls have access to a quality education and modern contraceptives, it enables women to exercise the choice to have smaller, healthier families, reducing emissions well into the future."[287] Educating women means giving them the ability to advocate for themselves. This is particularly important in relation to climate change, since women are often in a position to devise and implement the most effective adaptation strategies.

Education can start by simply raising awareness of climate change. In some areas of Somalia, many clan-related conflicts are primarily political, but have been exacerbated by the effects of climate change and the degradation of the environment. How to raise these climate-related issues in a conflict-sensitive way when working with affected communities is of key importance for environmental peacebuilding. In the large states of Hirshabelle and Galmudug in central Somalia, the Berghof Foundation has been working to strengthen *infrastructures for peace* and foster dialogue as a first step in educating people about the effects of climate change.[288] As part of this initiative, members of different communities work together to raise awareness of the impact that both climate change and environmental degradation are having on them as individuals and communities. Local people's knowledge that the severe droughts, failing harvests and starving livestock they have had to contend with are in fact all part of a global phenomenon, and not limited to their particular region, has until now been very limited. This underlines the importance of climate change education, not just in its own right but also as a tool for conflict resolution.

Berghof's aim in these two states of Somalia is to help create a common understanding of this problem: to isolate climate change from the other grievances driving conflict, and instead open it up as an avenue for cooperation. Over the course of many interviews with local stakeholders, the project assesses community perceptions of the changing weather patterns and precisely how these patterns could be connected to the social and political grievances that they evidently exacerbate. This knowledge is gathered and synthesised to provide a comprehensive analysis of the climate-conflict dynamics at play, which can be discussed at community assemblies, known as *shirarka*. These meetings are intended as a setting for local dialogue and act as knowledge-sharing platforms among a diverse group of local stakeholders, thus helping to isolate the shared environmental issues from clan-based grievances. A radio show is also broadcast to increase knowledge of the impacts of climate change on local communities in Galmudug State and ensure that the awareness-raising reaches beyond those present at the *shirarka*.

By laying this foundation and promoting awareness of the environmental drivers, opportunities for the local conflict-sensitive initiatives that constitute the environmental peacebuilding process can then be discussed. Only after that can these initiatives be implemented to build resilience to climate risks, contributing to more peaceful inter-group relations and sustainable management of natural resources.

In all these approaches to environmental peacebuilding, there is a need for partnerships and integration among specialists across disciplines. The problems that cause climate insecurity in fragile and conflict-affected states lie at the intersection of the humanitarian, peace and development sectors (known as the "HDP triple nexus"). There are repeated demands for more integration within this triple nexus, as well as between all elements of the nexus and climate action. For a long time, the opportunity for cooperation has been slim. Limited information on how to proceed, or on the nexus risks at play, has held back comprehensive responses to climate change and conflict. But since the 2000s, understanding has grown as climate change has surged up the global agenda. Some organisations have adapted their work to include climate risks, creating more opportunities to integrate development, peace, humanitarian and adaptation programmes.

Progress on this is not yet where it needs to be, for various reasons. Inflexibility on the part of the donor community has limited what peacebuilding, development and environmental actors can do. Funding meant to address the climate-conflict nexus has often been divided between silos. Requests for funding can get bounced around between peace, development, humanitarian and climate agencies. Organisations may apply for funding from a humanitarian donor, who then takes the view that this is primarily a development project. And when it is taken to a donor that prioritises development, it may well be disregarded on the grounds that, actually, it is more of a stabilisation or peace-related project. Project applications end up on a merry-go-round, exacerbated by the frequent internal strategy reviews carried out by donors seeking an impossible symmetry between how their organisation is structured and how the world actually works in practice.

The process in recipient countries is by no means straightforward either. While some governments are now discussing climate and security at the behest of specific donors, they may, in reality, seek more immediate solutions to their core needs.[289]

There are some signs of change, however. In 2022, the G7 countries issued a statement on Climate, Environment, Peace and Security, spurring the launch of the Weathering Risk Peace Pillar. This consortium project initiated by the German Federal Foreign Office has seen significant resources put into addressing climate and security. The five pilot projects operate in Somalia, Iraq, Yemen, Nigeria and the Bay of Bengal, and, for two years,[i] will gain insights into best practices and make recommendations on how to mainstream climate and security to support peace processes on the ground. Extending projects such as these beyond the timeframes conceived for the pilot phases will be crucial for learning how to make the best use of resources in this area.[290]

Interdisciplinary collaboration will also be important in the years ahead. In Somalia, Berghof has partnered with two UN agencies, the International Organization for Migration (IOM) and UNEP, in a consortium to accommodate the scale and diverse needs of a comprehensive climate and security project. Each actor brings expertise and resources in the fields of migration, the environment and peacebuilding, and aims to address the violent conflicts over natural resources, stabilise the affected communities, and manage natural resources. This should leverage more funding for practical action and mobilise the relevant expertise. However, this is not a solution that is applicable in all contexts. Creating a large consortium often means a slower process and more bureaucratic hassle. Alternatively, donor agencies could support single organisations by making funding more flexible to accommodate the range of required activities. With the prospect of more climate finance becoming available in the coming years, this may also provide additional space and flexibility to actors looking to work on these challenges. But some of this financing should be directed at environmental peacebuilding and dialogue efforts as a way of promoting adaptation in fragile settings.

---

i The Peace Pillar is implemented by Adelphi, in partnership with three peace organisations and a fifth organisation to conduct impact assessments (Innovations for Poverty Action). Of the peace organisations, Berghof Foundation is implementing two projects in Somalia and Iraq, the European Institute of Peace is conducting a project in Yemen, and the Centre for Humanitarian Dialogue is working in Nigeria and the Bay of Bengal. Lessons from these projects have provided the basis for parts of this book.

Just as there have been some limited advances in environmental peacebuilding, there are now the beginnings of a parallel approach in mediation and peacemaking. In 2022, the UN's Policy and Mediation Division published a practice note on the implications of climate change for mediation and peace processes.[291] This important note discussed *climate-informed mediation*, whose purpose is to engage conflict parties and help them to find a sustainable solution to their dispute. It made the point that most of the UN's special political missions and peacekeeping operations are situated in contexts marked by dual vulnerability: high climate exposure and fragility. Even if climate change is not a core issue in a dispute, addressing its effects can create entry points for technical cooperation, confidence- building over natural resource management and, eventually, possible peaceful conflict resolution.

The UN paper suggested highlighting opportunities for shared benefits and new income sources. These would include introducing climate-related negotiation tracks, inviting climate experts and private sector representatives to workshops to inject innovative ideas, and technological solutions. The aim would be to see how prevention, adaptation and mitigation measures can be brought into the negotiation process to generate incentives for collaboration, compromise and peace dividends. Building shared water infrastructure was presented as one example of how to shift parties' focus from political stalemate to technical cooperation.[292]

Another proposal from the UN was to encourage the drafting of climate-adaptive agreements that would take into consideration the future impacts of climate change. This is based on sound reasoning: without such adaptiveness, agreements may be rendered irrelevant within a few years. For instance, changing rainfall patterns could rapidly undermine an agreement on seasonal migration. By maintaining a degree of flexibility, drafters could allow for adjustments to climate-related sections of agreements. Similarly, they should avoid climate-blind provisions that may inadvertently increase vulnerabilities or reduce resilience to climate change.

This change in thinking, bringing climate and environment to the fore in peace processes, is important, as the case of Colombia demonstrates. Before the peace accord with the government in 2016, FARC guerrillas had greatly limited logging, partly to provide continued tree-cover from air raids by government forces. But shortly after their weapons were handed over, the deforested area – used primarily for cattle ranching and coca production – increased by 44 per cent.[293] Since then, the destruction has continued as other rebel groups have piled in; the 49,600 hectares of primary forest loss in 2015 more than doubled to 128,000 in 2022. The environment had been considered a beneficiary of the peace process at the time of its negotiation, but what came afterwards was very different.

A new approach is showing some signs of success, however, as the new government led by Gustavo Petro seeks to bring 'total peace' into effect. Rather than regarding the environment as an incidental beneficiary of peace (which failed to materialise), the new approach is to present it as central to the negotiations. A moratorium on deforestation even became the entry point for talks between one rebel group, Estado Mayor Central (EMC), and the government. Given that many major Amazon regions, such as Guaviare, Caquetá and Putumayo, are controlled by the EMC and other rebel groups, engaging with them on the environment during the peace process will be an important move in guarding against the environmental setbacks suffered by Colombia in 2016.[294]

There are lessons here for future agreements in this sphere. Proposing shared climate-related goals or initiatives in a draft agreement could help to promote trust and cooperation. It could encourage the establishment of early warning and dispute resolution mechanisms that address potential conflicts fuelled by climate stress. Conversely, failing to give sufficient consideration to these issues in the drafting of peace agreements may increase the level of environmental degradation. Increasing scientific knowledge (and its effective communication) may help to bring climate change to the fore in such negotiations. As the authors of the UN paper conclude, "peace processes that incorporate climate considerations can simultaneously help advance both peace and climate action."[295]

It is also important to consider, particularly in environmental peacebuilding strategies, how climate change might be perceived by conflict parties. In many contexts mentioned in this paper, there may be limited understanding of climate change. And even where knowledge is available, there may be a reluctance to engage on it out of conviction that it represents some kind of Western agenda, or even that it is irrelevant to the conflict. Whether or not one agrees on either point, this is an interesting lesson, and one that should be considered when working on environmental peacebuilding.

The Centre for Humanitarian Dialogue (HD) has been working in the Sahel since 2015, supporting mediation between farmers and herders. In the tri-border area between Mali, Niger and Burkina Faso, these two groups regularly come into conflict over poorly marked land borders, water sources and transhumance routes. With the challenges of climate change and increasingly scarce resources, these conflicts are becoming more common.

As one HD expert, Michael Vatikiotis, has described it, "tribes and clans who once shared resources are now fighting over dwindling fish ponds that supply important protein or receding pasture lands where herds of goats and cattle graze." Mediation helps to defuse some of these conflicts, although more training for local conflict management is required, not least because climate change will 'turbo-charge' ethnic and religious divisions and spur violence as a reflexive response to displacement and migration. Some of the areas involved are controlled by extremist armed groups, but they cannot be abandoned to "chronic lawlessness as that will mean surrendering to advancing desertification and the loss of tree cover", which would make the land infertile and accelerate temperature rise.[296]

Over the past eight years, HD has supported a network of local mediators across this region (expanding to Chad and Mauritania); they now number almost 2,000 in the cross-border areas. Of the 759 conflicts identified between 2016 and 2019, almost half were resolved by local leaders and mediators.[297] The way in which HD and mediators have approached the issues around natural resources also provides some interesting lessons. Even though climate change is relevant to these resources, it can appear as an external agenda. In exchanges with stakeholders, HD has found that participants are more receptive to framing the topic as the 'environment', due to its connection to more tangible phenomena.[i] HD's experience in the Sahel underlines the importance of tuning one's approach to reflect the participants' perceptions.[ii]

Similarly, Natasha Hall of CSIS has pointed out that more needs to be done to link environmental protection to people's daily concerns, as this approach is more likely to strengthen their commitment to change. For instance, diesel generators in places like Iraq cause cancer and other diseases, as well as emitting greenhouse gases, while untreated wastewater can pose major hazards to public health. In Basra in 2018, to take an example referred to in Chapter 3, tens of thousands of people needed to be hospitalised after contracting water-borne diseases. Connecting what many people see as the less tangible issue of climate change with local 'real-world' concerns would help to increase acceptance of the climate agenda.[298]

The potential of environmental peacebuilding to support climate adaptation should not be underestimated. Its remit is broad, ranging from natural resource management to transforming social and political relationships with the environment. With more support, both political and financial, it should be an important element in minimising climate risks in areas affected by ongoing, or the legacies of, violent conflict.

---

i One 2022 case demonstrates some progress in this area, and potentially points to a way forward. In Nasarawa State in Nigeria, where farmer-herder conflicts are common, Awe and Azara communities have signed a peace pact around natural resource use, in support of the National Livestock Transformation Plan – a mechanism to modernise livestock production and reduce tensions in conflict zones. The agreement includes commitments to mainstream climate adaptation, demonstrating the possibilities of including climate factors in peace agreements.

ii There are signs of change, however. In recent years, there has been increasing awareness of climate change, and peace agreements have responded accordingly. See, for instance, a recent agreement in Nigeria supported by HD which recognises climate change and includes provisions on climate adaptation and climate-smart agriculture.

8 Ukraine: the intersections

Nobody would claim that Russia's motivation for invading, occupying and seeking to eradicate the idea of Ukraine as a nation in February 2022 was related to climate change. Directly or even indirectly. This does not mean, however, that there are no climate considerations in the way the war has played out since then, even if they are very different from those relevant to other regions covered in this book, such as the Sahel, the Horn of Africa, and Mesopotamia.

In Ukraine, the war has had a highly visible impact on the environment. Wide-scale destruction has been caused either deliberately by the Russians, or as collateral damage by both sides. Often this is because of a sustained artillery bombardment not equalled anywhere since the Second World War. The resulting pollution, damage and destruction of rivers, forests, soil and reservoirs are likely to take decades to restore and remedy.[299]

During the Soviet era, the Irpin River, which runs to the west of Kyiv was dammed. In late February 2022, when Russian forces were advancing on Kyiv, the Ukrainian army opened the dam, flooding the area and blocking the Russians' route to the capital.[300] [i] The Russians also used the threat of environmental destruction to gain some semblance of military advantage in Ukraine. They mined a dam at the Kakhovka hydroelectric power plant, which threatened 80 downstream settlements including Kherson. Elsewhere, they toyed menacingly with the memories of the Chernobyl disaster (now known in Ukraine as Chornobyl) by occupying the Zaporizhzhia nuclear plant, causing international concern about potential nuclear fallout, moving heavy military vehicles that raised nuclear dust and caused a spike in gamma radiation levels.

Developments took a dramatic turn for the worse in the summer of 2023, when Russian forces destroyed a significant part of the Kakhovka Dam. This led to the flooding of hundreds of thousands of hectares of Ukraine's most fertile agricultural land, causing widespread economic, agricultural and ecological damage expected to last for years after the war ends. The destruction of the dam, and the deaths and devastation it caused, provided additional impetus for efforts by a group of international lawyers to include 'ecocide' among the crimes that can be prosecuted at the International Criminal Court. Although not yet considered alongside other well-known war crimes spelled out in Article 8 of the Rome Statute, this term has been used since 1972, when Olaf Palme, the Swedish Prime Minister, used it to describe acts which had a "substantial likelihood" of causing "severe and widespread damage to the natural environment".[302] Since then, the International Committee of the Red Cross has produced its "Guidelines on the Protection of the Natural Environment in Armed Conflict". It suggests how international humanitarian law can be interpreted to address such environmental crimes, and how this must be supported at the national level to be effective. In Ukraine, ecocide already features in domestic law; under Article 441 of its criminal code, "mass destruction of flora or fauna, poisoning

i A new term, "warwilding"", has been coined to describe "the creation or sometimes even the destruction of habitat as a result of the tactical manipulation of nature" or "using nature in warfare". Both forms (creation and destruction) have been seen in Ukraine in recent months. The Ukrainian flooding of Irpin led to the Russians' abandonment of much military equipment, but also a restoration of a large area which – seven decades earlier – had been a wetland ecosystem and biodiversity hotspot. Conversely, the Russian destruction of the Nova Kakhova Dam in June 2023 and the subsequent flooding created major damage to both agriculture and ecology.[301]

of the atmosphere of water resources, as well as committing other actions that can cause and environmental catastrophe" is a criminal offence. But without a complementary international legal framework, the likelihood of Russian leaders or forces being prosecuted for such crimes is slim.

There have been some important moves, which can be expected to grow in scope as part of the wider global move towards environmental justice and accountability, to hold Russia responsible for the damage it has inflicted on Ukraine. Not surprisingly, President Volodymyr Zelensky has often called for post-war environmental recovery and condemned what he terms the ecocide committed by the Russians. Even during the first year of the fighting, a number of efforts were initiated to gather data and evidence regarding the environmental damage, with a view to helping Ukraine eventually to sue Russia for reparations dedicated to environmental restoration. One such example is the work of The Reckoning Project, an organisation working on justice and accountability for war crimes in Ukraine, using meticulous methodologies for gathering legally admissible evidence. There are few conflicts where the environmental dimension of warfare has received so much attention.[i]

Then there is the destruction of Ukraine's great forests. By mid-2023, the World Wildlife Fund (WWF) was estimating that 280,000 hectares of forest had been destroyed in the war; it put the costs of environmental reconstruction at US$51 billion.[303] During the same period, one fifth of Ukraine's national parks and nature reserves were affected, an important point given that although Ukraine accounts for six per cent of European territory, it contains 35 per cent of the continent's biodiversity.[304]

To counter this, various methods of financing Ukraine's post-war environmental reconstruction have been advanced. The EU's Social Climate Fund, which supports decarbonisation in countries outside the EU and whose Carbon Border Adjustment Mechanism (CBAM) will from 2026 impose fees on a list of imports into the EU, is

---

i Environmental issues featured in the Gulf wars and in Kosovo, and their aftermath, but less systematically.

one example. An initiative being discussed is that CBAM could help pay for Ukraine's post-war recovery, ensuring that it is as sustainable as possible, by imposing taxes on Russian products entering the EU (while also contributing to Russia's own eventual decarbonisation through the use of incentives).

Another possibility is that Ukraine could be recognised by the US and EU as a potential supplier of decarbonised energy for the EU, in contrast to Russia's traditional role, and that it could act as a substitute for Chinese green energy supply chains by providing hydrogen to Europe. The Ukrainian government is also being encouraged to push carbon-free energy as a vital element in the massive investment drive that will be needed to fund its post-war reconstruction.[305]

In addition to environmental restoration, it is also important that the overall reconstruction of Ukraine's cities, housing and infrastructure is carried out in an explicitly green way, enabling the country's previously extractive and carbon- intensive economy to transition to a net zero one. Such scenarios for a vastly more sustainable post-war future for Ukraine were considered at the Ukraine Recovery Conference in Lugano in July 2022, and are high on the agenda of the OECD and EU.

*****

The clearest connection between the Ukrainian war and climate change is the conflict's impact on energy markets and greenhouse gas emissions. In the days after the invasion, the West imposed restrictions on Russian energy exports, which pushed up global energy prices. The express intention of Western European nations was not just to punish the Russian government, but also to replace Russian fuel supplies with alternative ones.

The decisions necessary to bring about this replacement were accompanied by much self-criticism, especially in Germany. People looked back, in some bewilderment, over the way Europe had increased its dependence on Russia even after the invasion and annexation of the Donbas and Crimea in 2014. Imports of Russian gas as a proportion of gas consumption in the EU had increased from 36 per cent in 2015 to 41 per cent three years later, labelled by one observer (in a view shared by many) as "the strategic blunder at the heart of Europe's energy policy" that permitted Moscow to "weaponise its dominant position" in Europe's energy market.[306]

As gas prices soared, some governments – including the UK, France, Italy and Germany – responded in semi-panic mode by re-opening or extending coal mines. Others such as India and China increased coal production for electricity, even though coal emits double the amount of carbon dioxide per unit of energy compared to gas. Several other countries made efforts to accelerate the exploration and extraction of gas. In the first six months following the Russian invasion, greenhouse gas emissions in Europe went up, in large part owing to the increasing use of coal over gas. This soon changed, however, as we will see below.

The conduct of the war itself was also bad for the climate. Large militaries are massive emitters, especially when involved in 'kinetic' actions, when whatever motivations commanders might have for conserving energy are significantly reduced. It is estimated that in the first year of the war alone, an additional 100 million tonnes of carbon dioxide equivalent were emitted by the war effort of the countries involved.[307] In addition, there were emissions from burning forests and leakages after the Nordstream gas pipelines from Russia to Western Europe were sabotaged.

A further harmful effect of the war was that it shifted public and official attention away from climate issues, disrupting ongoing multilateral efforts to curb emissions. Commentators reasonably questioned whether Europe's climate leadership and decarbonisation priorities were under threat. Diplomatic cooperation on climate issues suffered a setback, global subsidies for fossil fuels rose, and Russia (in the face of sanctions) became both more reliant on its oil and gas revenues and even more determined to block progress in international negotiations regarding the transition to net zero.[308] Similarly, governments found themselves paying more for defence, food and fuel, which had a negative effect on aid budgets when combined with rising inflation, debt and inflation rates. This in turn has led to budgetary cuts for development programmes whose purpose is to reduce conflict and promote climate adaptation.

Equally significantly, although in a more indirect connection between climate and conflict, the Ukraine war introduced new tensions in relations between the G7 countries and many countries of the Global South. There were various reasons for this; one was that countries outside Europe resented what they regarded as an excessive Western focus on Ukraine at the expense of other ongoing conflicts, such as in Afghanistan, Ethiopia, Sudan, Syria and Yemen.

The Indian External Affairs Minister Subrahmanyam Jaishankar expressed this view when he declared, "Europe has to grow out of the mindset that Europe's problems are the world's problems, but the world's problems are not Europe's problems."[309] This touched on various grievances, including perceptions of hypocrisy and the failure of the wealthier countries to honour their commitments on climate finance. Others were the hoarding of vaccines during the Covid-19 pandemic, restrictive and unfair immigration policies (which contrasted with the welcoming of 'white' refugees fleeing Ukraine) and the repeated double standards noted by many observers. As an editorial in the Financial Times in June 2023 put it, "Muslims across the Middle East note that the west has vigorously countered Russia's seizure of parts of Ukraine, but has long been muted in its reaction to Israel's creeping annexation of the West Bank." If the US and Europe want countries elsewhere to join their condemnation of Moscow, the article continued, they "must avoid appearing hypocritical."[310] These charges of double standards – which escalated dramatically in the face of Israeli actions in Gaza, following the Hamas terrorist atrocity in October 2023 – made it easier for countries seeking to find some benefits for them from the war to justify why they should be allowed to avail themselves of low-cost purchases of Russia's fossil fuels. The result of those purchases has been to reduce what might otherwise have been a positive impact of Western sanctions on reducing global carbon emissions.

Another aspect related to the Global South's grievances against countries of the West is what one analyst has termed Putin's efforts to "weaponize the crises of the Anthropocene" for geopolitical goals, as Russia attempted to do by limiting the supplies of grain and fertiliser to poorer countries. He did this – via his threats to attack grain ships in the Black Sea – while trying, with more success than was justified, to blame the West for the shortages.

As also noted in Chapter 4, this was likely part of Putin's strategy to sow as much chaos as possible in the West's 'near abroad' (mainly the Middle East and North Africa). The hope was that greater hunger and hardships in such countries would provoke further large-scale migration to Western countries, benefiting Russian-supported populist and anti-immigrant parties in those countries. The greater "the strains on environmental and commodity ecosystems, the more opportunities" actors such as the Wagner Group would have to exploit them by causing destabilisation, as they successfully managed to do in Mali, Sudan and elsewhere.[311]

One particularly important effect of the Ukraine war relates to the severe additional food insecurity that climate change had already brought to some parts of the world, such as Somalia. Food shortages in the Horn of Africa were made considerably worse by the interruption of Russian and Ukrainian exports of both grain and fertiliser. Much of the 11 million tonnes of wheat that the war prevented from reaching the global markets had been destined for the world's poorest countries. Food insecurity, whether caused either by climate change or conflict (or in this case a mixture of both) on other continents, especially Africa, is likely to lead to growing tensions and new forms of conflict. That food insecurity is compounded still further by the additional defence costs of the Ukrainian war, which have led many Western governments to reduce the funds available for humanitarian assistance and food aid to the poorer nations.[312]

If the problems relating to the Ukraine crisis can be felt in the hottest and driest countries on earth near the Equator, they are also in evidence in the Arctic, another region with serious implications both for climate and geopolitics. In Chapter 2 of this book, there was a brief discussion of the Arctic Council and how it has been undermined by the conflict in Ukraine. In 2023, the Foreign Minister of Finland, Pekka Haavisto, expressed his concern that gridlock in the Arctic Council could lead to "an Arctic with no rules or an Arctic area with no common goal for climate change", adding that it would then be free for everyone to use for shipping and extraction of raw materials. In some ways, the very existence of the Arctic Council can be seen as an example of multilateral environmental peacebuilding in the most rapidly warming region of the planet. The eight members of the Council (the five Nordic countries, plus US, Canada and Russia) have tried to keep wider tensions out of their discussions, sometimes using the slogan of "high north, low tension" to indicate the need for a cooperative approach in efforts to solve the environmental and economic issues of the region.[313]

Balanced against the various negative impacts relating to climate (quite aside from the humanitarian, human rights, economic and political consequences), there is one area where it is possible to be optimistic. Although, as we have seen, the initial response to the invasion involved an increase in emissions and prices because dirtier energy sources were used, this trend was soon reversed. From August 2022 to January 2023, gas consumption in the EU fell by nearly 20 per cent, a substantial drop that derived not only from the far higher energy prices that followed the invasion but also solidarity with the Ukrainian cause and the desire to reduce consumption so as to avoid strengthening the Kremlin leadership.[314]

Similarly of importance was the push that the war gave to the transition to renewable energy. Several governments, especially in Europe, reacted to the energy disruption not just by increasing the (short-term) search for accessible fossil fuels, but also by accelerating their move to renewable energy. Prior to the Russian invasion, which came as discussions about ambitious targets were already under way, the EU had been seeking to reduce emissions by 40 per cent, and also to reach the target of 32 per cent of energy from renewable sources by 2030. Afterwards, partly reflecting the importance of ending the bloc's reliance on fuel from Russia, EU leaders significantly increased the targets to 57 per cent (up from 40 per cent) for reduced emissions and 45 per cent (up from 32 per cent) for renewable energy sources by 2030.[315]

The President of the European Commission, Ursula von der Leyen, said that avoiding Russian oil and gas would be the right thing to do "not only for the climate, but also ... to gain independence and to have security of energy supply."[316]

Similarly, the Ukraine war and China's support for Russia brought added impetus to the Biden Administration's US$369 billion Inflation Reduction Act, providing subsidies for domestic producers in light of the need to reduce US dependence on China's production of solar panels (which accounts for up to 80 per cent of the world's supply, up from what had been a mere 10 per cent in 2010).[317]

The International Energy Agency estimates that the major surge in renewable energy in 2022 and 2023 (and beyond) has come from a happy combination of governmental support, energy security concerns and the increased competitiveness of renewable technology.[318] The Russian invasion thus seems likely to have a lasting positive impact in one area at least: accelerating investment in renewable energy as a product of governments' need to achieve greater energy security, which is likely to have a knock-on effect by creating economies of scale and pushing down costs further.[319] [i]

One analysis from Oxford University also suggests that this rapid green transition by 2050 will bring trillions in net savings.[321] It is indeed encouraging that many governments seem to have concluded that their hard energy security needs dovetail with, rather than diverge from, their 'softer' climate change mitigation aspirations, in that the

---

i This is undeniably important. But one cannot help feeling that some commentators may slightly overdo their enthusiasm. One, Michael Orenstein, has written, "Attempting to win recognition as Putin the Great by uniting the Slavic lands of Russia, Belarus and Ukraine, Russian President Vladimir Putin may be hailed instead as Putin the Green, the man who convinced Europe to give up dependence on fossil fuels." *Politico*'s assessment was similar, in October 2022 awarding Putin first place in their list of environmental influencers, pronouncing that he had "done more than any other single human being to speed up the end of the fossil fuel era".[320]

energy security which many hanker for will depend on developing domestic renewable energy sources and reducing their dependence on fossil fuels. However, it is essential to ensure that these benefits do not solely serve the interests of the wealthier countries, while countries in Africa and part of Asia lack the capital resources and technical knowledge to scale up renewable technologies such as solar and wind power.[322]

Aside from the disastrous effects on the people of Ukraine, the consequences of the Russian invasion have been negative on various fronts, including by weakening international resolve and the consensus to reduce greenhouse gases. The short overview of issues presented in this chapter illustrates the complexities of the relationship between conflict, climate and other forms of environmental degradation.

Since February 2022, Ukraine has been suffering under a form of warfare that combines the worst aspects of the 20th century, with grinding attrition, trench warfare and saturation artillery bombardments, and those of the 21st century, with long-distance precision missiles launched against cities, mass drone attacks, cyber- disinformation and other sophisticated techniques. In this sense, the course of the war is unlike the conflicts in East and West Africa, the Middle East, and South Asia. After all, in all those situations, climate change has played a role in making the situation worse, adding a level of hardship to grievances that make war more likely, and then making any resolution of the conflict even harder to bring about.

That was not the case with Ukraine. Climate change was not responsible for President Putin's illegal invasion and the war crimes that have followed, but there are connections between that conflict and the global problem of climate change. Understanding those connections and working to blunt the harsher consequences, especially those that fall on the developing world, will be a central issue for G7 countries. This is because those countries are increasingly realising they need to come to terms with the fact that, however justified and necessary they feel their support for Ukraine against such unprovoked aggression to be, they have not managed to convince much of the rest of the world. Taking a more vigorous stance on climate issues – in terms of reducing emissions and helping poorer countries adapt to climate change impacts – will be one of the principal means of reducing the widening gap between 'the West and the rest'. The entire field of climate and security has, therefore, suddenly taken on a new and additional meaning, even if many policy-makers do not seem to have grasped this yet.

9 Conclusions and ways forward

The renowned historian of Eastern Europe, Timothy Snyder, has drawn a perceptive parallel between the Holocaust and climate change. With Hitler's ability to persuade Germans that permanent hunger lay in store for them unless they conquered the countries to the East to satisfy their alleged need for *Lebensraum*, he demonstrated that: "When an apocalypse is on the horizon, waiting for scientific solutions seems senseless, struggle seems natural, and demagogues of blood and soil come to the fore." The Nazis were thus able to present a future crisis as justification for immediate draconian measures against sectors of their own people.[i]

The comparisons with the present are worryingly easy to follow: with major shortages of food or land a likely result of climate change, nations or communities could well be tempted or even encouraged to blame others for their suffering. For Snyder, the starvation in Somalia and the genocide in Rwanda in the mid-1990s were a dreadful

i The Ukrainian historian Serhii Plokhy wrote that with its reputation as the breadbasket of Europe and with the highest concentrations of Jews, "Ukraine would become both a prime object of German expansionism and one of the Nazis' main victims". As we have seen in the previous chapter, the Nazis were not the last to treat Ukraine as the object and a victim of a neighbour's expansionism, or to use comparably dishonest propaganda to justify it.[323]

foreshadowing of what climate change might bring to Africa. The first "exemplified death brought directly by climate, and the second, racial conflict brought by the interaction of climate and political creativity". Though criticised by some reviewers as being exaggerated (one rival, presumably feeling rather foolish since 2022, mocked what he called Snyder's "speculation" about Chinese or Russian wars of conquest in search of resources as being "wild in the extreme"), the parallel should be taken seriously.[324] There is indeed a considerable risk that climate change will be a potent driver of ever-greater violence and conflict.

One of the two main aims of this short book is to help illustrate the various truths relating to climate change, the environment, conflict and security. These linkages can be expected to have a growing impact on us all, and this is why they matter so much. The other aim is to offer some indications of how we might go about dealing with them. The ways in which climate affects conflict differ according to the geographical, socioeconomic, and political situation, so any adaptation responses will need to be similarly varied and customised.

History is replete with examples of communities failing to react to major threats – environmental or military – with sufficient seriousness or speed. Similarly, at various times in the past, changes in climate have had negative impacts on humanity. Evidence suggests that these impacts have often been linked to violent conflict. But even if climate change has never been the primary cause of such conflict, it has certainly been a contributory or multiplying factor – by exacerbating the other causes, whether economic inequality, political exclusion, ethnic division, poverty or food shortages. But whatever impact climate has had on conflict in the past (debated as it has been), this is likely to be little guide for predicting future impact, given the expected increase in the speed of climate change in the coming decades.

Even under far worse climatic conditions, the direct and proximate cause of war is always – and will remain – the human decision to take up weapons and use them. The stated and actual reasons for doing so vary and may stem from ideology, greed, hunger, hate, ambition, fear, or the desire to throw off (or impose) oppression or occupation. War is never inevitable, although once it has started, the other side usually has little or no option but to fight back. What we can say, however, is that when societies are already fragile from human or natural causes – be it disasters, violence, inequality, poverty, corruption or incompetence – the effects of climate change will make conflict harder to avoid and harder to resolve.

The situation today is different in one important respect from anything historians have uncovered about the past. While climate change has long affected humankind, the reverse has almost never applied. Humans have not previously had the ability to alter the actual climate,[i] although they have had a major impact on their natural environment.

Now in the Anthropocene, there can be no doubting that the relationship is one that we may term as mutually abusive. And mutually abusive on an epic scale. Through its greenhouse emissions, mainly in the past half century, humanity has unwittingly altered the climate – not just locally, as sometimes happened in the past, but globally. In turn, that human-altered climate is going to impact the world's population to such an extent that no community or ecosystem on the planet will be unaffected.

The most cited links between climate and conflict tend to concern the loss and degradation of land, often related to water shortages. One key UN paper on the topic summed it up as follows: the shifts

---

i One of the few major exceptions put forward to the belief that only since the present era has humankind affected climate change comes from a study by University College London in 2019. This concluded that "the Great Dying of the Indigenous Peoples of the Americas resulted in a human-driven global impact on the Earth System in the two centuries prior to the Industrial Revolution." It has long been known that the population of the Americas was devastated by the arrival of belligerent settlers from Europe who killed millions of them through conflict and the diseases they brought with them. But only recently has it been proposed that the eradication of so many people led to significant natural reforestation of formerly agricultural land (equivalent to the size of France), leading to the capture and absorption of carbon dioxide which, in turn, brought global temperatures down by 0.15 per cent.[325]

On the other hand, Peter Frankopan described the theory of man-made climate change in this situation as ingenious but "speculative and problematic". He questioned both the population and the reforestation statistics on which it was based, and suggests that the global cooling that took place (referred to in Chapter 2 of this book) was more likely to have been caused by non-human factors such as volcanic eruptions that we know happened at precisely that time.[326]

resulting from climate change "may contribute to the loss of livelihoods, forced displacement, stresses on institutional capacities and disruptions or breakdowns in the delivery of public services, ultimately undermining the ability of society to productively manage and resolve tensions and disputes."[327]

Rising sea levels are another inevitable feature of rising temperatures because global warming leads to the melting of polar ice sheets. The increased rate of sea-level rise, as UN Secretary-General António Guterres warned the Security Council in early 2023, threatens to cause "a mass exodus of entire populations on a biblical scale". But it is not just climate migration that will ensue; rising seas, he said, are a threat multiplier, damaging lives, economies and infrastructure, with dramatic implications for global peace and security.[328]

There has been progress in achieving recognition that climate change acts in ways that magnify the risks and intensity of insecurity and violent conflict. Notwithstanding the failure to adopt the draft Security Council resolution on this topic in 2021, and the likelihood that Russia will continue to veto any far-reaching proposals as part of that body, the international community as a whole seems to be on track to recognising the need to counter these risks. This is progress, even if both limited and late in the day.

One region where the overlapping crises of social fragility, climate change and violence are especially stark is the Sahel, which for several years has been under attack from two very different cross-border threats: climate change and Islamist terrorism. Climate change has increased the frequency and intensity of extreme weather events, such as droughts and floods. As seen in the example of Lake Chad, as fodder and water are becoming scarcer, local communities that once depended on rain-fed agriculture have come into conflict with pastoralists.[329] However, political and economic marginalisation seems to play an even more significant role than climate change, with a lack of economic prospects not only causing many young people to seek opportunities elsewhere, but also increasing the influence of armed groups.

It is a similar situation in Syria; as discussed earlier, agricultural policies decided in Damascus had long made life much more challenging in rural regions of the country. But in 2011, when the protests began, the farmers deprived by the government's policies had just weathered a long and intensive drought. Many understandably chose to down tools and re-settle in towns and cities. Three years later, ISIS insurgents appeared in the almost-deserted villages, where their recruitment drive was fuelled by economic desperation and various grievances with the government, including the atrocities carried out in response to the Arab Spring. Jihadist groups like ISIS, Boko Haram in the Sahel, and al-Shabaab in Somalia are able to feed off the hardships and discontent that are caused in part by climate change. The outcomes – when combined with corruption, repression and other forms of poor governance – are extremist terrorism, insurgency and civil war in several countries.

There are instances where we are already seeing the direct impact of climate change on conflict-affected areas. But one area where climate-related conflict risks are often overlooked is the energy transition. Climate risk is going to be a major feature of countries whose stability will be threatened by the necessary move away from fossil fuels. In other words, such countries are doubly impacted by climate change not just because of climate change itself; but even more because of the measures that need to be undertaken in response to climate change, especially the transition away from oil.

Any such transition will be destabilising enough in countries of the Global North.[i] But particular attention will need to be paid to states (such as Iraq, Libya and Nigeria) which are not only already on the front line of climate change and conflict, but which – because their governments' revenues are so overwhelmingly based on oil production – are also going to pay a steep price in budgetary terms as a result of humankind's need to move away from fossil fuels.

---

i The financial repercussions if the market value of fossil fuel companies collapses as a result of the energy transition are likely to be immense, including a banking crisis necessitating bail-outs that are being estimated in trillions of dollars, dwarfing the crisis of 2008 and with potentially dramatic implications on social stability.[330]

*****

The link between climate change and conflict is presented almost invariably, and rightly so, as the former contributing in various ways to the latter. Writers, thinkers and scientists have rarely paused to consider the other direction: the impact instead that conflict can have on the climate. We have noted from the previous chapter a very indirect set of negative consequences for the climate emanating from the war in Ukraine due to the war's environmental destruction and impacts on emissions, seen in the temporary return to coal, and reduced focus on net zero as a realistic goal.

Looking at the climate-conflict connection this less common way round, some have maintained that the greatest threat comes from nuclear warheads and the impact this would have in destroying the ozone layer, causing a 'nuclear winter' and a drop in temperature that would pose an even greater threat to food security and human survival.[331] While logically possible, it seems a less likely outcome than an ever hotter world contributing to more conflict. Moreover, one can imagine that frightening line of thought giving rise to truly apocalyptic conclusions, and even being posited as a mad and perverse 'solution' to the global warming that is caused by climate emissions.

From another angle, it is apparent that climate change has sometimes been neither the agent of conflict, nor even of collateral damage, but an actual military *goal* in itself. Military superpowers (mainly but not solely the US) have sought to manipulate the climate and weather patterns through artificial means in order to achieve a strategic advantage. In the 1950s, the US military believed that weather modifications could bring significant benefits. Indeed, one reason for proceeding with scientific experiments in this field was the fear that the USSR might achieve a breakthrough earlier and negatively affect the weather over Western countries. According to this thinking, in the global stand-off embodied by the Cold War, military-induced control of the climate would enable one side to cause either flooding or drought in regions under the other side's control.[332]

As seen above in the chapter on environmental peacebuilding, plans in this vein continued until the early 1970s, when opinion, including in the US Senate, turned against them. The destruction of the Nova Kakhovka Dam in Ukraine in June 2023 was a variant of this strategy, although the aim here was to achieve a military advantage not through artificial modification of the local climate, but through the use of strategically placed high explosives to trigger an environmental disaster.

In some quarters there is sensitivity about the use of the term 'climate security'. This is understandable given the propensity of some Western politicians and militaries to see threats merely in terms of national security. It means that the responses have often taken the form of threatening deterrents, brutal measures, human rights violations and cheap nativist populist rhetoric against desperate migrants and refugees fleeing the realities of climate change in their homelands. Notwithstanding the vital importance of avoiding such a crude framing of how climate change and security intersect (this crude framing is essentially what people refer to when they say they oppose 'securitising' the climate debate), it would be a mistake to give the impression that climate change and security are not closely linked, when it is very clear that they are.

There are two main reasons this linkage and its significance should not be denied. The first is that certain actors in the security sphere have the capacity to play a key role in advancing the cause of climate mitigation and climate adaptation. When the US Department of Defense or the UN Security Council, to take two of the more obvious examples, gets involved in highlighting the climate change threat and trying to do something about it, that should be welcomed (albeit guardedly, in light of governments' tendency to focus on hard military measures instead of a more enlightened and long-term approach). After all, confronting the greatest challenge to humanity – not to mention standing up against those who persist in denying that reality – will require the broadest coalition of interests ever assembled. Excluding actors from the common effort solely on the grounds that they are military-or security-focused would be self-defeating and a wasted opportunity.[i]

The second reason not to discourage discussion of climate and security together is that there are forms of security (notably *human security*) which are less threatening, and at the same time more central to far greater numbers of people than narrower concepts of national, state or regime security. The current government of Germany has successfully married the concepts. In March 2022, the incoming Foreign Minister, Annalena Baerbock of the Greens, stressed that climate issues were central to securing "the fundamental necessities of our lives". This applied to the country's domestic security, to be sure, although not in the sense of achieving that security by preventing people from fleeing to Germany from climate disasters in other parts of the world, but rather in terms of protecting the German people from floods and heatwaves at home. Baerbock went on to say that it was also highly relevant to the country's security at an international level, where the impacts of climate change affect geopolitics and supply chains. This would necessitate an approach that places the protection of human rights and safeguarding livelihoods at the centre of security policy considerations (i.e. human security), including the protection of vulnerable groups in areas worst affected by climate change.[333] In short, the topic of climate and security may employ a very different concept of security to the one traditionally understood. This one is a long way from the notion of security that was applied by those who advocated, say, for the disastrous global war on terror or the deployment of French paratroopers to prop up African dictators, or more recently, for the building of walls and other harsh measures to keep out migrants fleeing environmental catastrophe.

---

i One can find a roughly analogous debate over protecting the rainforest, some adherents of which have been tempted to reinforce their arguments by pointing out that rainforests are useful in health and commercial terms since they provide ingredients for, say, cancer drugs. But just because people may use these arguments in an attempt to persuade non-nature lovers of the material benefits of conservation, it does not mean that the former do not see much wider value in conserving nature. Similarly with the use of security arguments to bring in new allies to the cause of climate action: just because some people may use these arguments to win over new supporters does not mean they are only capable of seeing climate through the narrow prism of 'securitisation'.

*****

One of the issues that we will all soon have to face up to in the climate-conflict nexus is mass migration. At the World Humanitarian Summit in 2016, the UN agreed to the concept of the humanitarian-development-peace (HDP) 'triple nexus'. But a new triple nexus between conflict, climate change and migration is likely to become a source of equal concern very soon, with some already recognising it as a new threat that needs to be taken seriously. Migration, the last of those three elements, is the outcome of the other two. And this being the case, attention will need to focus much more on addressing the negative consequences of the destabilisation of the regions from which people will be forced to flee, and on responding to the far greater numbers of migrants and refugees seeking to enter the countries of the G7.

It is rightly seen by some as a perverse irony that many of Europe's far-right parties – which are opposed both to immigration and to action on the climate emergency – are keenly aware that they will in fact benefit from the influx of people fleeing the climate crisis. Despite these parties' deep hostility to immigration, they know that they gain more electoral support when higher numbers of immigrants arrive in their countries. As the signs of climate change become even more obvious, there is a distinct possibility that such parties will cease to be strict climate change deniers, and instead turn towards some form of 'eco-fascism'. Should this happen, their agenda is likely to advocate harsh military measures to keep out the desperate migrants who were forced to leave their homes precisely because of climate denialism in the Global North.[334] It is no coincidence that President Putin's government believes it will be the strategic beneficiary of the resulting destabilisation and violence in Western countries, and that most of these far-right parties happen to support the Kremlin's 'values' and war aims in Ukraine and, in turn, receive backing from Moscow.

In the legal domain, there are welcome signs of progress in providing greater protection for migrants and refugees fleeing climate disasters in their homelands. This is reflected in the readiness of various UN bodies to start considering such people as 'genuine' refugees, even when they are obliged to leave their home countries not because they are at risk of persecution from human agency, but rather because of climate-induced ecological breakdown. Some national courts are now taking a similar view.

But changes in international and national law are only one of three possible pathways for resolving the difficulties presented by climate migration. The second lies in providing greater incentives to persuade people that there is indeed a hopeful future for them where they currently are, and that there is therefore no need to migrate. Well-targeted and properly funded adaptation measures, especially around improved agricultural techniques, have a key role to play here.

The third way to handle the migration challenge is to mentally prepare the populations of receiving states to accept that the arrival of climate refugees is an inevitability. Despite signs of hope shown by countries such as Sweden and Germany in 2016, there can be no illusion that this will be anything other than extraordinarily difficult. To help avoid social conflict in destination countries, sustained education and cultural dialogue on why the refugees have been compelled to leave their homes (including the attribution of responsibility for emissions), and how they can be of great benefit to the host society, will be key components of this dialogue.

Legal protection for refugees and a less hostile environment in receiving countries are, of course, interdependent since the law will ultimately reflect political reality. If migration continues to be widely seen in destination countries as politically unacceptable, then both national and international law will presumably be changed or abandoned. Therefore, the most reliable approach is likely to be the second one – addressing the causes of climate migration through mitigation and adaptation measures. The goal of preventing some of the departures could then be achieved. Many politicians in receiving countries will consider the reduction of the number of migrants via such measures to be essential for their own political survival and domestic harmony.

*****

Until now, climate change on its own has not been the principal cause of conflict or large-scale migration. In 2022, the IPCC concluded that socioeconomic and governance factors still play a more central role than climate change in causing conflict. Issues relating to corruption, inequality, repression and conflict tend to make the impact of climate change much worse than they would otherwise have been.

At the same time, as global heating further intensifies, the consequences of weather and climate extremes will increase vulnerabilities and tensions that make intra-state conflict more likely.[335] The World Weather Attribution Group recently estimated that anthropogenic climate change made the 2022–2023 drought in southern Ethiopia, southern Somalia and eastern Kenya 100 times more likely. However, they stress that food insecurity and strife in these regions were largely driven by poverty and state fragility, and not just by the weather [336] This diagnosis will change as climate effects become more extreme, but recognition of the role of political factors, and of human decision-making more broadly, should also provide some hope. By working to support communities (with capacity-building, mediation, finance and all the tools we have available), there are several ways in which we can alleviate climate- and conflict-related risks.

Climate risk needs to be systematically incorporated into all aspects of strategic thinking, in a way it manifestly is not at present. Increasing the level of ambition in programmes designed to promote climate change mitigation (especially the causes of fossil fuel emissions) and adaptation (to alleviate the effects of climate change) will of course be a massive undertaking, with few people expressing optimism that they will ever suffice. They will also need to be complemented by a new perspective that includes conflict in the equation. At the very least, this means ensuring that whatever is proposed in the areas of both mitigation and adaptation is designed to minimise conflict, rather than unwittingly serving as a cause of new conflicts or a compounding factors in existing ones. It is also important to continuously monitor the impact on the human rights of all parties concerned, given that the causes of intra-state conflict lie almost invariably in violations of human rights that have led to the marginalisation and alienation of particular groups who are then motivated to take up arms.

Understanding the pressures that can lead to conflict, and how they will be affected by climate change in each specific local context, will help communities facing acute climate-related challenges adapt to them. Interventions targeted at the social changes caused by environmental pressures must – if they are to successfully boost resilience – be driven by the communities themselves, who need to be fully convinced of their relevance, and then supported by external actors. What is needed, therefore, is development assistance that is simultaneously conflict-sensitive, rights-based and environmentally sustainable. Achieving all of that within the same programming is much easier said than done. One promising area (as indicated in Chapter 4, on climate migration) lies in focusing aid and climate finance on agricultural programmes in conflict and climate-risk areas. The fact that such programmes may serve as a form of adaptation that could help persuade some would-be migrants to remain in their places of origin might make it easier to obtain external funding for them.

After years of often justified criticism of its lending being insufficiently climate-, conflict- or human rights-sensitive, the World Bank has announced various measures which it hopes will lessen that reputation. "We cannot endure another period of emission-intensive growth," declared its new President Ajay Banga in July 2023. The Bank stated that it would allow countries hit by disasters, including climate-related emergencies to pause repayments on loans; it also announced the launch of a crisis facility to offer concessionary funds to the lowest-income countries.[337]

There is much that can be done in the new field of environmental peacebuilding to support adaptation in regions that are badly affected by climate change, conflict, or both simultaneously. As a practice, this inverts the usual climate-conflict discussion by looking to engage with environmental issues as a means for achieving peace, rather than seeing them as a factor in fanning conflict. Looking at this topic in greater detail reveals an array of approaches that fall under the 'environmental peacebuilding' umbrella. Each of them has the potential to support communities in mitigating some of the cross-cutting risks of climate change and conflict.

Using examples from the Middle East, Europe and Africa, Chapters 6 and 7 outlined some of the successes that have been achieved in this area. One example in the DRC demonstrated how focusing on gender can prove to be a transformative approach when addressing conflicts over water – a finding also borne out in some of the UN's work in Yemen.[338] In Somalia, the Berghof Foundation's work in awareness-raising and education has enabled communities to better mediate conflicts around natural resources, harnessing improved understanding about climate change as a tool for resolution. Advances in knowledge or practice at this intersection of mediation and climate change can empower communities to peacefully manage conflict in the years to come.

Anyone involved in peacebuilding knows how difficult it can be to operate in conflict areas. But the costs of not doing so – whether the goals of the people concerned are to promote peace, social cohesion or climate adaptation – are even greater. The current political climate and discourse around aid levels make it hard to imagine serious increases in climate finance in the immediate future. The mechanisms that disburse these limited funds are becoming better at absorbing risks and reducing barriers for conflict-affected states to access them, but much more is required. Funding for adaptation must be secured using ingenious new mechanisms or existing structures such as blended finance.[i] This is going to be an uphill task as long as investment in conflict-affected areas continues to lack incentives due to their inherent political instability and weak governance – which are anathema to investors, of course. But that does not mean it is any less important to work to find ways around these impediments.

---

i Blended finance, as defined by the OECD, is "the strategic use of development finance for mobilising additional finance towards sustainable development in developing countries. It attracts commercial capital towards projects that contribute to sustainable development, while providing financial returns to investors. This innovative approach helps enlarge the total amount of resources available to developing countries, complementing their own investments and ODA inflows to fill their SDG financing gap, and support the implementation of the Paris Agreement."

A longer-term approach is also essential, and not that hard to implement. And yet several donors limit their support for peacebuilding projects in climate-affected regions to two years or even less. It is extremely difficult to successfully implement activities and work in highly insecure environments within these short donor-driven timeframes, especially given that peacebuilders are dealing with inter-communal tensions that might go back decades or more.

*****

Western countries, which tend to be the main funders of work in the areas of peacebuilding, climate and security, need to be constantly aware of the growing understanding in the developing world of the truth underlying climate justice, namely that the nations which are worst affected by climate change, as well as by conflict, are not only among the poorest countries of the world, and therefore least likely to have the economic and governance resources to carry out successful resilience and adaptation programmes. They are also the countries that have contributed least to the emissions that have caused climate change – itself a factor which partly explains their poverty.

Some of the more affluent countries, having industrialised earlier and emitted billions of tonnes of carbon in the process, were able – precisely because of their new wealth – to wage conflicts thousands of miles away from their capitals, bringing warfare, expropriation and decades of colonial occupation to nations whose descendants are still paying the price for what was done to them in the 19th and 20th centuries. On top of that, there is a relatively unknown component that seems sure to develop into a major aspect of the discourse. A significant portion of the financial capital that underlay both the Industrial Revolution (which caused emissions) and the colonial empires (seen by many to have kept parts of the world more under-developed than they would otherwise have been) derived from the labour of enslaved African populations in the Americas.

There seems curiously little appreciation of that grisly concatenation of circumstances. Western and other more affluent or heavily emitting countries (China, the Gulf States, Israel, etc.) seem unwilling to comprehend why poorer countries, which developed industrially either later or never, may be so reluctant to pay heavily for climate finance or adaptation, with the latter group strongly believing it to be the responsibility of the richer countries.

The resentments are going to grow as the planet heats up, especially given that climate financing pledges made by the developed world 15 years ago are still not fully honoured. Populations from the countries most affected by climate change – understandably – do not appreciate being lectured on how to adapt to it. But when this lecture is delivered by the very countries which have historically contributed most to climate change and still reap the benefits of fossil fuels, the injustice and hypocrisy ring even louder. Particularly at a time when multilateralism is being eroded by great power competition and emerging conflicts deepen international divides, the need to exhibit national humility and profound sensitivity on this topic is greater than ever.

Central to this need for national humility (which involves some reckoning with their history and how it negatively affected others, which is a process few countries are willing to engage in, with Germany a notable exception) on the part of the richer and higher-emitting countries is some form of embracing the ethos of 'climate justice'. As explored in Chapter 1, this concept relates to the injustice that arises from the impacts of climate change on those countries that are least responsible for causing it. It also relates to future generations which are penalised for their predecessors' unwillingness to act. When it comes to conflict-affected countries, this injustice is particularly stark. Africa has been the preponderant focus of climate and security research. Yet the historical carbon emissions of the entire continent amount to under four per cent of the global total. Somalia, for example, is currently facing one of its most severe droughts, which comes after decades of civil conflict, although it has contributed practically nothing to the global total.[339] [i]

---

i Indeed, as the *Economist* has put it, the Somali people have emitted roughly as much carbon dioxide since independence in 1960 as Americans have in the past two and a half days.[340]

One way in which climate policy attempts to address this is through the 'polluter pays' principle. This is, in theory, the idea that whoever releases harmful greenhouse gas emissions should bear the costs of managing their impact on human society and the environment. The reality is that this principle is consistently violated; in the eyes of developing nations, climate conferences have so far more closely resembled what former UK Prime Minister Gordon Brown has called a "filibuster" and "broken promises" on the part of wealthier nations, rather than a meaningful attempt to engage in reparations.

Brown called for an approach to help developing countries cut their emissions that does not derive from notions of charity. Rather, it should be based on the polluting nations' ability to pay, considering their historical liability, using global taxes like airline or shipping levies and the innovative use of guarantees offered to regional development banks by the richest countries. Such an approach also involves cancelling the unpayable debt of low-income countries in return for those countries taking action on climate. Another proposal for helping poorer countries with their strategies for both mitigation and adaptation includes impact investing to fund clean or renewable energy, for which governmental support would be required to encourage companies to measure the social and environmental benefits of their activities.[341] The IMF estimates that between 80-90 per cent of climate funding will need to come from the private sector. If that is even remotely correct, there will need to be a radical improvement in the conditions that could bring the private sector to the table, often in the form of guarantees from governments and multinational banks.[342]

There have been some advances in addressing climate change in multilateral formats, especially with the agreement on Loss and Damage at COP27 in November 2022. If the commitments made there are followed through, there should soon be a mechanism to address the needs of the most vulnerable countries. To date, it cannot be seriously claimed that the wealthy nations that have profited from emissions are meaningfully supporting those regions most affected by these emissions.

The same applies to the fossil fuel companies, most of which are based in developed countries. A study released in May 2023 – the first attempt to quantify the economic burden caused by individual extracting companies – estimated that the 21 largest polluters will be responsible for over US$5 trillion of losses from drought, wildfires, sea-level rise and melting glaciers. This would mean that those companies owe US$209 billion in annual climate reparations to compensate the worst-affected communities.[343] These are vast sums, although they are probably at the conservative end of the spectrum. It goes without saying that the companies concerned will go to almost any lengths (including via well-funded campaigns of disinformation, for which they will find willing allies among populist politicians and media owners) to ensure that their shareholders should not be burdened by the obligation of paying any compensation at all for the damage they have done. This will continue to be the case, however justified and however great the needs of communities affected by both climate change and conflict.

*****

Such predictable obstructionism does not have to mean that those companies will always manage to avoid accountability, even if they have been remarkably successful to date. In addition to advances in some multilateral formats, there has been significant progress in the field of climate attribution and litigation. If the first component of climate justice is action taken via Loss and Damage to compensate countries most affected by more affluent states' emissions, the second is litigation.

This is a relatively new field of activity, but one that seems certain to grow exponentially as more and more people conclude that action in the courts may be one of the few avenues capable of producing results in the form of heavy penalties, and ultimately serious action, on the part of polluters nervous at the prospect.[344] Given that the outcomes of political and diplomatic wrangling at COP and other major international meetings are distinctly underwhelming, it is not surprising that some stakeholders are pursuing legal channels to hold governments and polluting companies accountable for their failure to act.

Litigation (and, above all, the threat of it) seems to be one of the few accessible and also effective ways to prevent climate change and rising temperatures from reaching levels that are too high to be borne by large sections of the world's population. A potentially important step in this regard came in March 2023 with the adoption of a UN resolution requesting an advisory opinion of the International Court of Justice (ICJ). If followed up, the findings of the ICJ could increase the risk of litigation for states that fail to take action, by identifying "a standard or benchmark for what is expected of states."[345] Future defendants may be expected to include Western governments which have done relatively little to counter the threat, and the fossil fuel corporations (at least some of which have known since the 1970s exactly what the emissions from their fuels would do to the planet, but then hid the evidence and repeatedly lied about it). It is conceivable, too, that some of the chief purveyors of false information and climate change denialism, such as Rupert Murdoch's media empire, which includes Fox News, may also be targeted.[i] Since legal disputes can be seen as an alternative to armed conflict, the development of litigation in this sphere may be regarded as a positive benefit in promoting climate action in new and effective ways and, ultimately, in preventing social conflict.

The costs of climate litigation were initially covered by private activists and NGOs, supported either by wealthy philanthropists or crowd-sourcing. Increasingly, however, some investors have come to regard climate-related legal claims as a potential source of profit. Although it would seem vastly preferable that the beneficiaries from such claims should be the victims from vulnerable communities, as opposed to hedge fund managers motivated solely by profit, it is

---

i Although this is less likely to take place in the US than elsewhere, owing to the First Amendment's protection of free speech even when it is a case of deliberately peddling falsehoods. The role of Rupert Murdoch himself is hard to over-estimate. When, in September 2023, he resigned from his position as chair of his media group, there was an intense outpouring of anger from the climate community. One quote may suffice, because it is so representative of others' opinion. Dr Peter Gleick said Murdoch's "distortions have influenced policymakers and the public and wasted critical time that should have been spent slowing the climate crises we now see all around us. His influential outlets ... have been spewing ... deep climate disinformation, and they continue to support and promote biased, misleading opinion pieces and commentary from climate deniers and delayers ... When our history is written, and the final roster of climate villains is posted, Murdoch will be at the top."[346]

nevertheless encouraging that such hard-headed investors now see which way the wind is blowing.

As the litigation option gains traction, polluting and high-emitting companies increasingly have reason to fear being held to account (a wholly new experience for many of them). Recent studies by the London School of Economics and UNEP have drawn attention to the negative effects on stock market valuations when a new climate lawsuit is filed or a new settlement reached. For example, in 2021, when a court in The Hague ordered Shell to cut its global emissions by 45 per cent by 2030, its share price fell by 3.8 per cent. Encouragingly (depending on one's perspective), BP's annual report issued in April 2023 warned investors that legal proceedings "could reduce our financial liquidity and our credit ratings".

Such developments – combined with a clamping-down in Europe on companies accused of 'greenwashing', i.e. not being sufficiently committed to climate transition, or spreading misinformation – create a scenario in which companies and governments alike are going to have to do more.[i] This is especially so given that some of the cases currently before the courts (including proceedings against multinational giants such as Chevron and Shell) may lead to substantial awards, possibly unleashing an even larger flurry of lawsuits to follow. Moreover, as a UNEP report put it, as climate litigation increases in frequency and volume, the body of legal precedent will grow, forming "an increasingly well-defined field of law."[348]

---

i Misinformation can come in many forms. These days it is less likely to appear as outright climate change denial. That shift happened as the evidence has become ever more irrefutable. A newer form is for the mega- polluters to pose as the champions of the world's most vulnerable people, including in countries with conflict. In 2013, the CEO of Exxon Mobil, Rex Tillerson, claimed that fossil fuels were actually of benefit to development. "What good is it to save the planet if humanity suffers?" he piously asked, saying that reducing oil use to reduce emissions would make it harder to lift two billion people out of poverty. Similarly, ten years later, the Chief Executive of Shell declared that cutting oil and gas production would be "dangerous and irresponsible" and that children in Pakistan would have to "study by candlelight". There was no intended irony in him saying this just days after the planet had suffered its hottest June ever, and only a year after Pakistan had experienced devastating floods as a result of the climate change that came from carbon emissions.[347]

Appealing to the moral imperative of wealthier nations has had little effect so far. Resistance on the part of their politicians, officials, media and oil companies, justified by what some continue even now to call their 'scepticism' towards the clear scientific consensus, has prevented real action to mitigate greenhouse gas emissions. There is certainly likely to be a far greater chance of action once the cascade of impacts on wealthy nations prompts a tardy rethink. When Western value chains are cut off by climate disasters in affected regions, when export markets collapse into instability or terrorism, and when vast numbers of desperate migrants arrive at their borders, these countries are likely to find that both their moral conscience and their strategic interests are conveniently served by supporting human security and adaptation in the most vulnerable areas, especially those in conflict.

*****

Nobody can afford to wait, however, for that Damascene or ultimate reality moment: whenever it is that those countries most responsible for emissions finally take sufficient action to mitigate them. In the meantime, there is an urgent need to focus attention on the areas of the world that are most affected by climate change and conflict. For countries facing both curses at once, the likely results are not hard to predict: greater immiseration, poverty, destabilisation, radicalisation and migration on a hitherto unprecedented scale.

This book has attempted to point out various approaches that can lessen these impacts. Incorporating the perspective of climate risk into all sectors of political and economic activity, especially areas where new or renewed conflict seems probable, is one of them. Another is to support appropriate adaptation programmes in conflict areas to a far greater extent, as these regions are the most vulnerable.

Similarly, environmental peacemaking and peacebuilding offer many advantages. There may be as yet relatively few examples to point to, and therefore only a limited number of lessons that can be drawn from them for the benefit of future forays. But that is mainly because environmental peacebuilding is still quite new. Important opportunities are thus being missed. If donors were to decide to scale up activities and build up national and international capacities, it would have a knock-on effect beyond new pilot areas in conflict-affected regions. Testing innovative environmental peacebuilding approaches could provide results of great value elsewhere. New forms of farming that are more resistant to climate change, for instance, offer many benefits in the diverse areas of mitigation, adaptation, peace-building, sustainable development, and addressing root causes of migration (through making existing lives and livelihoods more feasible). Targeting the agricultural sector for investment is therefore an obvious starting point, and one likely to yield the highest dividends.

Since we can be almost certain that more conflicts will erupt in places where the effects of climate change exacerbate grievances within and between communities, it is especially important to train insider mediators to help reduce or prevent such conflicts. Preparedness for peaceful co-existence – adaptation by another name – both in the countries of origin and in the countries hosting greatly increased numbers of refugees (dismissing them as 'migrants' will not make the issue go away) will be of critical importance in reducing further conflict.

In short, there is a colossal challenge ahead. It is essential to address the burning, but hitherto far-too-ignored, issue of ensuring that climate change does not lead to ever greater cycles of conflict. Work is needed on many fronts, but focusing attention and resources on those regions of the world that are most threatened by both climate change and conflict must be a crucial component of the overall climate strategy.

There is no need to wait for additional data and no reason not to act immediately. All that is required is the political will to put it in motion. The usual arguments will be of course be deployed: that the hard science data is not yet 'conclusive'; that there is less need to hurry than 'alarmists' make out; that the linkages between climate on the one hand, and either conflict or migration, on the other (always apparently made by 'elitists' in our midst) are not properly established; that 'private capital' and the 'market' will soon come up with clever new solutions at some time in the future, thereby obviating the need to try to solve the problem now; and that we should focus on problems 'closer to home' rather than justifying the move of 'migrants' from 'far-away' countries. We know all too well what we can expect.

Those arguments can be countered. And they need to be. It is axiomatic that acting now will lessen the problems that humanity everywhere will face further down the road. The combined challenge of climate change and conflict is indeed daunting in its scope and complexity. But it is not insuperable. Facing the two together, as a single threat rather than as two separate, even disconnected problems, will make this supreme task of our generation more achievable.

Bibliography

Books, book chapters and academic journals

Akçalı, E., & Antonsich, M. (2009). "'Nature Knows No Boundaries': A Critical Reading of UNDP Environmental Peacemaking in Cyprus". *Annals of the Association of American Geographers*, 99(5), 940-947.

Baechler, G. (1999). *Violence through Environmental Discrimination*. Social Indicators Research Series: Volume 2. Kluwer Academic, Dordrecht.

Battisti, D. S., & Naylor, R. L. (2009). "Historical Warnings of Future Food Insecurity with Unprecedented Seasonal Heat". *Science*, 240-244.

Bellemare, M. F. (2015). "Rising food prices, food price volatility, and social unrest". *American Journal of Agricultural Economics*, 97(1), 1-21.

Bhandari, A., Thakuri, S., Koirala, P., & Devkota, M. P. (2021, December). "Conflict-Sensitive Climate Change Adaptation in Nepal: An Analysis of Climate Resilience Policy Frameworks". *Journal of Forest and Livelihood*, 20(1), 31-44.

Bhavani, R. R., & Lacina, B. (2015). "The effects of weather-induced migration on sons of the soil riots in India". *World Politics*, 67, 760-794.

Bowles, D. C., Butler, C. D., & Morisetti, N. (2015). "Climate change, conflict and health". *Journal of the Royal Society of Medicine*, 390-395.

Buhaug, H. (2010). "Climate not to blame for African civil wars". *PNAS*, 107(38), 16477-16482.

Burke, M. B., Miguel, E., Satyanath, S., Dykema, J. A., & Lobell, D. B. (2009). "Warming increases the risk of civil war in Africa". *PNAS*, 106(49), 20670-20674.

Burt, M., & Keiru, B. J. (2011). "Strengthening post-conflict peacebuilding through community water-resource management: case studies from Democratic Republic of Congo, Afghanistan and Liberia". *Water International*, 36(2), 232-241.

Busby, J. W. (2022). *States and Nature. The Effects of Climate Change on Security*. Cambridge: Cambridge University Press.

Carey, M. (2014). "Beyond Weather: The Politics and Culture of Climate History". In A. C. Isenberg, *The Oxford Handbook of Environmental History* (pp. 23-51). Oxford: Oxford Academic.

Conca, K., & Dabelko, G. D. (2002). *Environmental Peacemaking*. Baltimore: Woodrow Wilson Center with Johns Hopkins University Press.

De Juan, A. (2015). "Long-term environmental change and geographical patterns of violence in Darfur, 2003-2005". *Political Geography*, 45, 22-33.

Diamond, J. (2005). *Collapse: how societies choose to fail or succeed*. New York: Viking.

Falkner, R. (2023). "Weaponised Energy and Climate Change: Assessing Europe's Response to the Ukraine War". *LSE Public Policy Review*, 3(1).

Fletcher, T. (2022). *Ten Survival Skills for a World in Flux*. London: William Collins.

Frankopan, P. (2023). *The Earth Transformed*. London: Bloomsbury Publishing.

Friedman, T. (2008). *Hot, Flat, and Crowded: Why We Need a Green Revolution - and How It Can Renew America*. New York: Farrar, Straus and Giroux.

Ghimire, R., & Ferreira, S. (2015). "Floods and armed conflict". *Environmental and Development Economics*, 21(1), 23-52.

Gilmour, A. "Preventing climate change is a human rights issue". *Bloomberg*, 2 February 2020.

Gilmour, A. and Edenhofer, O. "Neue Allianzen gegen Klimakonflikte", *Frankfurter Allgemeine Zeitung*, 12 August 2021.

Goodell, J. (2023). *The Heat Will Kill You First*. Boston MA: Little, Brown and Company.

Homer-Dixon, T. (1991). "On the Threshold: Environmental Changes as Causes of Acute Conflict". *International Security*, 76-116.

Homer-Dixon, T. (1999). *Environmental Scarcity and Violence*. Princeton: Princeton University Press.

Ide, T. (2020). "The dark side of environmental peacebuilding". *World Development*, 127, 1-21. Ide, T., Bruch, C., Carius, A., Conca, K., Dabelko, G. D., Matthew, R., & Weinthal, E. (2021).

"The past and future(s) of environmental peacebuilding". *International Affairs*, 97(1), 1-16. Jia, R. (2014). "Weather shocks, sweet potatoes and peasant revolts in historical China". The Economic Journal, 92-118.

K.C., S. (2013). "Community Vulnerability to Floods and Landslides in Nepal". *Ecology and Society*, 18(1).

Kalilou, O. (2021). "Climate change and conflict in the Sahel: the acacia gum tree as a tool for environmental peacebuilding". *International Affairs*, 201-218.

Kaplan, R. D. (1994, February). "The Coming Anarchy". *Atlantic Monthly*, 273(2), 44-76. Kennett et al. (2022). "Drought-Induced Civil Conflict Among the Ancient Maya". *Nature Communications*, 13(3911).

Ki-moon, B. (2021). *Resolved: Uniting Nations in a Divided World*. New York: Columbia University Press.

Koch, A., Brierly, C., Maslin, M. M., & Lewis, S. L. (2019). "Earth system impacts of the European arrival and Great Dying in the Americas after 1492". *Quaternary Science Reviews*, 207, 13-36.

Koubi, V. (2019). "Climate Change and Conflict". *Annual Review of Political Science*, 22, 343- 360.

Koubi, V., Bohmelt, T., Spilker, G., & Schaffer, L. (2018). "The Determinants of Environmental Migrants' Conflict Perception". *International Organisation*, 72(4), 905-936.

Krampe, F. (2017). "Toward Sustainable Peace: A New Research Agenda for Post-Conflict Natural Resource Management". *Global Environmental Politics*, 17(8), 1-8.

Krampe, F., Hegazi, F., & VanDeever, S. (2021). "Sustaining peace through better resource governance: Three potential mechanisms for environmental peacebuilding". *World Development*, 144.

Krampe, F., Smith, E. S., & Hamidi, M. D. (2021). "Security implications of climate development in conflict-affected states implications of local-level effects of rural hydropower development on farmers in Herat". *Political Geography*, 90.

Mach, K. J. et al. (2019). "Climate as a risk factor for armed conflict". *Nature*, 571, 193-197. Maertens, L. (2018). "Depoliticisation as a securitising move: the case of the United Nations environment programme". *European Journal of International Security*, 3(3), 344-363.

Mann, M. E. (2021). *The new climate war: the fight to take back the planet*. New York: Public Affairs, Hatchett Book Group.

Mares, D., & Moffett, K. (2016). "Climate change and interpersonal violence: a "global" estimate and regional inequities". *Climatic Change*, 297-310.

Maystadt, J.-F., & Ecker, O. (2014, March 25). "Extreme Weather and Civil War: Does Drought Fuel Conflict in Somalia through Livestock Price Shocks?" *American Journal of Agricultural Economics*, 96(4), 1157-1182.

McDonald, M. (2013). "Discourses of climate security". *Political Geography*, 33, 42-51. Nightingale, A. J. (2018, April). "Nepal's Towering Climate Adaptation Challenges". *Current History*, 117(798), 135-141.

Oels, A. (2012). "From 'Securitization' of Climate Change to 'Climatization' of the Security Field: Comparing Three Theoretical Perspectives". In J. Scheffran, M. Brzoska, H. G. Brauch, M. P. Link, & J. Schilling, *Climate Change, Human Security and Violent Conflict* (pp. 185-205). Berlin Heidelberg: Springer.

Parker, G. (2013). *Global Crisis: War, Climate Change and Catastrophe in the Seventeenth Century*. New Haven: Yale University Press.

Petraeus, D., & McAleenan, B. (2021, Spring). "Climate Change as a Growing Force in Geopolitics". *Environmental Affairs*, 8-17.

Rantanen et al. (2022). "The Arctic has warmed nearly four times faster than the globe since 1979". *Communications Earth and Environment*, 3(168).

Reuveny, R. (2007). "Climate change-induced migration and violent conflict". *Political Geography*, 26(6), 656-673.

Salehyan, I. (2014). "Climate and Conflict: making sense of disparate findings". *Political Geography*, 1-5.

Salehyan, I., & Hendrix, C. S. (2014). "Climate shocks and political violence". *Global Environmental Change*, 28, 239-250.

Selby, J. (2014). "Positivist Climate Conflict Research: A Critique". *Geopolitics*, 19(4), 829-856. Sinha et al. (2019). "Role of climate in the rise and fall of the Neo-Assyrian Empire". *Science Advances*, 5(11).

Soffiantini, G. (2020). "Food insecurity and political instability during the Arab Spring". *Global Food Security*, 26, 100400.

Steffen et al. (2015). "Planetary boundaries: Guiding human development on a changing planet". Science, 347, 1259855.

Striessnig, E., Lutz, W., & Patt, A. G. (2013). "Effects of Educational Attainment on Climate Risk Vulnerability". *Ecology and Society*, 18(1).

Vince, G. (2022). *Nomad Century: How to Survive the Climate Upheaval*. London: Allen Lane. Vivekananda, J., Schilling, J., & Smith, D. (2014). "Understanding Resilience in Climate Change and Conflict Affected Regions of Nepal". *Geopolitics*, 19(4), 911-936.

von Uexkull, N. (2014). "Sustained drought, vulnerability and civil conflict in sub-Saharan Africa". *Political Geography*, 43, 16-26.

von Uexkull, N., & Buhaug, H. (2021). "Security implications of climate change: a decade of scientific progress". *Journal of Peace Research*, 58(1), 3-17.

Werrell, C. E., Femia, F., & Sternburg, T. (2015). "Did we see it coming? State fragility, climate vulnerability, and the uprisings in Syria and Egypt". *SAIS Review of International Affairs*, 35(1), 29-46.

Werz, M., & Hoffman, M. (2016). "Europe's Twenty-first Century Challenge: Climate Change, Migration and Security". *European View*, 15(1), 145-154.

Wischnath, G., & Buhaug, H. (2014). "Rice or riots: On food production and conflict severity across India". *Political Geography*, 6-15.

Xu, C., Kohler, T. A., Lenton, T. M., Svenning, J.-C., & Scheffer, M. (2020, May). "Future of the human climate niche". *PNAS*, 117(21), 11350-11355.

Zhang, D. D., Lee, H. F., Wang, C., Li, B., Pei, Q., Zhang, J., & An, Y. (2011). "The causality analysis of climate change and large-scale human crises". *PNAS*, 17296-17301.

Reports of international non-governmental organisations

Abshir, S. (2023). "The Challenges of Climate Financing in Conflict Contexts". Brussels: European Institute for Peace.

Amnesty International and Afrewatch. (2016). "'This is what we die for'. Human Rights Abuse in the Democratic Republic of Congo Power the Global Trade in Cobalt". London: Amnesty International.

Beevor, E. (2020). "Caught in Climate Security Inaction". Washington DC: War on the Rocks.

Bosch, T., & Vinke, K. (2022). "Integrating Climate in Germany's National Security Strategy". Berlin: DGAP.

Buxton, N. (2021). "A primer on climate security. The dangers of militarising the climate crisis". Amsterdam: Transnational Institute.

Campbell, I. (2011). "Conflict sensitive approaches to local climate change adaptation in Nepal". London: Saferworld.

Climate Security Expert Network. (2019). "Climate-Fragility Risk Factsheet. Afghanistan". Berlin: Climate Security Expert Network.

Dabelko, G. D., Herzer Risi, L., Null, S., Parker, M., & Sticklor, R. (2013). "Backdraft: The Conflict Potential of Climate Change Adaptation and Mitigation. Environmental Change and Security Program". Wilson Center.

Druet, D., Lyammouri, R., & Mozersky, D. (2021). "From Renewable Energy to Peacebuilding in Mali. MINUSMA's Opportunity to Bridge the Gap". Stimson Center and Energy Peace Partners.

Eklow, K., & Krampe, F. (2019, October). "Climate-related security risks and peacebuilding in Somalia. SIPRI Policy Paper 53". Stockholm International Peace Research Institute.

Goodman, S., Guy, K., Maddox, M., Hansen, V. V., Sending, O. J., & Németh, I. (2021). "Climate Change and Security in the Arctic". Council on Strategic Risks and The Norwegian Institute of International Affairs.

Hadjimichael, M., & Papastylianou, K. (2019). "Environmental Protection and Cooperation in an (Ethnically) Divided Island: the Case of Cyprus". Oslo: PRIO.

HD. (2021). "Agro-pastoral mediation in the Sahel". Geneva: Centre for Humanitarian Dialogue.

Hillert, L. (2023). "Linking Conservation and Peacemaking". Geneva: Centre for Humanitarian Dialogue.

ICRC. (2020). "Guidelines on the Protection of the Natural Environment in Armed Conflict". International Committee of the Red Cross.

IDMC. (2023). "Global Report on Internal Displacement 2023. Internal Displacement and Food Security". Geneva: Internal Displacement Monitoring Centre.

Keating, M., Raasteen, J., & Brown, O. (2020). "Making Peace with the Climate: Conflict Resolution in a Climate-changing World". Brussels: European Institute of Peace.

Kool, D., Birkman, L., & Torossian, B. (2020). "Interprovincial Water Challenges in Iraq. Working Paper". Water, Peace and Security Partnership.

Lackner, H. (2021). "Climate Change and Conflict in Hadhramawt and Al Mahra". Berlin: Berghof Foundation.

Mansour, H., & Reiffenstuel, A. (2022). "The Jordan, Israel, and UAE Water-for-Energy Deal: Potential and Pitfalls of Energy and Water Sharing-Agreements in the Middle East". Amman: Konrad Adenauer Stiftung.

Michel, D. (2021). "Climate Security, Conflict Prevention, and Peacebuilding". Carnegie Europe. NUPI & SIPRI. (2021, February). "Climate, Peace and Security Fact Sheet: Somalia".

Orenstein, M. (2023). "Putin the Green? The Unintended Consequences of Russia's Energy War on Europe". Philadelphia: Foreign Policy Research Institute.

Pandey, N., Ruttinger, L., & Wolfmaier, S. (2020). “Climate Fragility Risk Brief: Nepal”. Berlin: adelphi.

Parr, A. (2022). “Making the Important Urgent. Can climate migration light up the slow-burn politics of the climate emergency?” Oxford Smith School of Enterprise and the Environment. Priestley, C. (2020). “The Peacebuilding Implications of Energy Transitions to a Carbon-Neutral Future”. Geneva: Quaker United Nations Office.

Sinha-Connolly, L. (2022). “Climate Change and International Security”. International Centre for Dialogue Initiatives.

Todman, W. (2023). “Powering Recovery. Reform, Reconstruction, and Renewables in Conflict- Affected States in the Arab World”. Washington DC: CSIS.

Vivekananda, J., Wall, M., Sylvestre, F., & Nagarajan, C. (2019). “Shoring Up Stability. Adressing climate and fragility risks in the Lake Chad region”. Berlin: adelphi.

von Lossow, T. (2016). “Water as Weapon: IS on the Euphrates and Tigris”. Berlin: Stiftung Wissenschaft und Politik.

von Lossow, T. (2018). “More than Infrastructure: Water Challenges in Iraq”. Clingendael.

WWF; BCG. (2023). “A Sustainable Economic Recovery for People and Nature”. World Wildlife Fund and Boston Consulting Group.

Reports from United Nations and related entities

Amu, N. (2020). “Addressing climate change–related security risks: The experience of a regional special political mission”. Oslo: Folke Bernadotte Academy and UNDP.

El-Hinnawi, E. (1985). “Environmental Refugees”. Nairobi: UNEP.

Gaston, E., Brown, O., al-Dawsari, N., Downing, C., Day, A., & Bodewig, R. (2023). “Climate- Security and Peacebuilding. Thematic Review”. New York: United Nations University Centre for Policy Research.

IOM. (2015). “Migrants Caught in Crisis: The IOM Experience in Libya”. Geneva: International Organisation for Migration.

IPCC. (2022). "Climate Change 2022: Impacts, Adaptation, and Vulnerability. Contribution of Working Group II to the Sixth Assessment Report of the Intergovernmental Panel on Climate Change. Summary for Policymakers". Cambridge University Press.

Ki-moon, B. (2009). "Climate change and its possible security implications: Report of the Secretary-General". New York: UNGA.

UNCCD. (2020). "The Great Green Wall. Press Kit". Bonn: United Nations Convention to Combat Desertification.

UNDP & CSM. (2021, December 14). "Climate Finance for Sustaining Peace: Making Climate Finance Work for Conflict-Affected and Fragile Contexts". New York: UNDP.

UNDP. (2016). "Human Security Handbook". New York: United Nations.

UNDP. (2017). "Journey to extremism in Africa". New York: United Nations Development Programme.

UNDP. (2020, October 12). "UNDP Climate Security Nexus and Prevention of Violent Extremism". United Nations Development Program.

UNDPPA. (2022). "The Implications of Climate Change for Mediation and Peace Processes. DPPA Practice Note". New York: United Nations Department of Political and Peacebuilding Affairs.

UNEP, UN Women, UNDP and UNDPPA/PBSO. (2020). "Gender, Climate & Security. Sustaining inclusive peace on the frontlines of climate change".

UN-ESCWA. (2022, October) "Countering economic dependence and de-development in the occupied Palestinian territory". Beirut: UN-ESCWA.

UNSOM and OCHR. (2017, December). "Protection of Civilians: Building the Foundation for Peace, Security and Human Rights in Somalia".

Other sources include numerous articles from Al Jazeera, The Economist, The Financial Times, The Guardian, The New York Review of Books, The New York Times and The Washington Post, among others.

Endnotes

1 Frankopan, P. (2023). *The Earth Transformed*. London: Bloomsbury Publishing. pp.655.

2 United Nations. "Hottest July ever signals 'era of global boiling has arrived' says UN chief": Available at: https://news.un.org/en/story/2023/07/1139162

3 Hillert, L. (2023). "Linking Conservation and Peacemaking". Geneva: Centre for Humanitarian Dialogue. p.14.

4 Paulson, H. "We must stop climate solutions from killing biodiversity". *Financial Times*, 16 July 2023.

5 For information on the planetary boundaries framework, see Steffen et al. (2015). "Planetary boundaries: Guiding human development on a changing planet". *Science*, 347, 1259855.

6 Lindsey, R., & Scott, M. "Climate Change: Arctic sea ice summer minimum." Available at: https://www.climate.gov/news-features/understanding-climate/climate-change-arctic-sea-ice-summer-minimum

7 According to figures sourced in: IEA. (2023). "CO2 Emissions in 2022". International Energy Agency.

8 Gilmour, A. "Preventing climate change is a human rights issue". *Bloomberg*, 2 February 2020.

See Klein, N. "From Blah, Blah, Blah to Blood, Blood, Blood". *The Intercept*, 7 October 2022; "Egypt, host of the UN climate summit, persecutes its own greens". *The Economist*, 9 November 2022; Kirchgaessner, S., & Lakhani, N. "Greenpeace accused of greenwashing Egypt's image ahead of Cop27". *The Guardian*, 30 October 2022.

9 Agence France Presse, "Climate crisis is greatest ever threat to human rights, UN warns", *The Guardian*, 9 September 2019.

10 Burns, W. "What U.S. intelligence needs to do today – and tomorrow". *Washington Post*, 7 July 2023.

11 Carey, M. (2014). "Beyond Weather: The Politics and Culture of Climate History". In A. C. Isenberg, *The Oxford Handbook of Environmental History* (pp. 23-51). Oxford: Oxford Academic. p.36.

12 See Diamond, J. (2005). *Collapse: how societies choose to fail or succeed*. New York: Viking. There has also been a recent advance in this regard by Kennett et al, who conducted a transdisciplinary case study combining archaeological, historical and paleoclimate datasets to explore the shifting relationships between climate change, civil conflict and the Maya's political collapse in the Yucatan Peninsula in the 15th century. It found that civil conflict increased significantly, with correlations between strife in the capital and drought conditions that led to food shortages which undermined the city's economic base. The study concluded by underlining "these complexities ... as we attempt to evaluate the potential success or failure of modern state institutions designed to maintain internal order and peace in the face of future climate change". See Kennett et al. (2022). "Drought-Induced Civil Conflict Among the Ancient Maya". *Nature Communications*, 13(3911). For a comparable analysis of the fall of the Assyrian Empire, see Sinha et al. (2019). "Role of climate in the rise and fall of the Neo-Assyrian Empire". *Science Advances*, 5(11).

13 Parker, G. (2013). *Global Crisis: War, Climate Change and Catastrophe in the Seventeenth Century*. New Haven: Yale University Press.

14 Ibid. pp.675-6

15 See endnote 12. p.34.

16 See endnote 1. pp.300, 391.

17 UNDP & CSM. (2021, December 14). "Climate Finance for Sustaining Peace: Making Climate Finance Work for Conflict-Affected and Fragile Contexts". New York: UNDP.

18 Ghafar, A. A. (2022). "The Return of Egypt? Assessing Egyptian Foreign Policy under Sissi". Doha: Middle East Council on Global Affairs.

19 Hall, N. (2023, June 26). "No Water Wars?" *Center for Strategic & International Studies*. Available at: https://www.csis.org/analysis/no-water-wars

20 Schroders Wealth Management. "Securing the supply of rare earth metals is central to our energy transition". Available at: https://www.schroders.com/en-us/us/wealth-management/insights/securing-the-supply-of-rare-earth-metals-is-central-to-our-energy-transition/

21 Gaston, E., Brown, O., al-Dawsari, N., Downing, C., Day, A., & Bodewig, R. (2023). "Climate-Security and Peacebuilding. Thematic Review". New York: United Nations University Centre for Policy Research. p.8.

22 McDonald, M. (2013). "Discourses of climate security". *Political Geography*, 33, 42-51.

23 White House Science Advisory Committee. (1965). "Restoring the Quality of our Environment. Report of the Environmental Pollution Panel". Washington DC: The White House.

24 See endnote 1. pp.588-591.

25 Ibid. p.623.

26 Homer-Dixon, T. (1991). "On the Threshold: Environmental Changes as Causes of Acute Conflict". International Security, 76-116.

27 Kaplan, R. D. (1994, February). "The Coming Anarchy". *Atlantic Monthly*, 273(2), 44-76. This was based on early research into this area, notably coming from North America. Meanwhile in Europe, more differentiated and less sensationalist viewpoints were also emerging: see the Environmental Conflicts Project (ENCOP) led by the scholar Günther Baechler, originally published in German. See also: Baechler, G. (1999). *Violence through Environmental Discrimination*. Social Indicators Research Series: Volume 2. Kluwer Academic, Dordrecht.

28 As reported in a review by journalist Toby Lester two years later. See Lester, T. (1996, August). "Beyond 'The Coming Anarchy'". *Atlantic Online*, August 1996.

29 Schwartz, P., & Randall, D. (2003, October). "An Abrupt Climate Change Scenario and Its Implications for United States National Security".

30 See endnote 23. p.46.

31 Buxton, N. (2021). "A primer on climate security. The dangers of militarising the climate crisis". Amsterdam: Transnational Institute.

32 Rantanen et al. (2022). "The Arctic has warmed nearly four times faster than the globe since 1979". *Communications Earth and Environment*, 3(168).

33 Goodman, S., Guy, K., Maddox, M., Hansen, V. V., Sending, O. J., & Németh, I. (2021). "Climate Change and Security in the Arctic". Council on Strategic Risks and The Norwegian Institute of International Affairs.

34 Rauhala, E. "An Arctic 'Great Game' as NATO allies and Russia face off in far north". *Washington Post*, 17 July 2023.

35 SIPRI. "World military expenditure passes $2 trillion for first time". Available at: https://www.sipri.org/media/press-release/2022/world-military-expenditure-passes-2-trillion-first-time

36 Crawford, N. C. (2019). "Pentagon Fuel Use, Climate Change, and the Costs of War". Providence: Watson Institute.

37 Belcher, O., Bigger, P., & Neimark, B. (2019). "Hidden carbon costs of the "everywhere war": Logistics, geopolitical ecology, and the carbon boot-print of the US military". *Transactions of the Institute of British Geographers*, 45(1)

38 Energy.gov. "Energy for the War Fighter: The Department of Defense Operational Energy Strategy". Available at: energy.gov/articles/energy-war-fighter-department-defense-operational-energy-strategy

39 Friedman, T. (2008). *Hot, Flat, and Crowded: Why We Need a Green Revolution - and How It Can Renew America*. New York: Farrar, Straus and Giroux. pp.317-22

40 See endnote 23. p.46.

41 UNDP. (2016). "Human Security Handbook". New York: United Nations.

42 UNHCR. (2021). "Climate Risk Profile – Sahel". Geneva: United Nations High Commissioner for Refugees: https://www.unhcr.org/61a49df44.pdf

43 Amu, N. (2020). "Addressing climate change–related security risks: The experience of a regional special political mission". Oslo: Folke Bernadotte Academy and UNDP.

44 Ki-moon, B. (2009). "Climate change and its possible security implications: Report of the Secretary-General". New York: UNGA.

45 UN "Security Council Fails to Adopt Resolution Integrating Climate-Related Security Risk into Conflict-Prevention Strategies". Available at: https://press.un.org/en/2021/sc14732.doc.htm#:~:text=The%20Security%20Council%20today%2C%20in, the%20risk%20of%20conflict%20relapse

46 Ibid.

47 Ki-Moon, B. "A Climate Culprit In Darfur". Available at: https://www.un.org/sg/en/content/sg/articles/2007-06-16/climate-culprit-darfur

48 Maertens, L. (2018). "Depoliticisation as a securitising move: the case of the United Nations environment programme". *European Journal of International Security*, 3(3), 344-363.

49 See Ki-moon, B. (2021). *Resolved: Uniting Nations in a Divided World*. New York: Columbia University Press. p.119. Also "Genocide all over again?" *The Economist*, 6 July 2023.

50 Oels, A. (2012). "From 'Securitization' of Climate Change to 'Climatization' of the Security Field: Comparing Three Theoretical Perspectives". In J. Scheffran, M. Brzoska, H. G. Brauch, M. P. Link, & J. Schilling, *Climate Change, Human Security and Violent Conflict* (pp. 185-205). Berlin Heidelberg: Springer. p.189.

51 NATO. (2022). "NATO 2022 Strategic Concept". p.6.

52 Petraeus, D., & McAleenan, B. (2021, Spring). "Climate Change as a Growing Force in Geopolitics". *Environmental Affairs*, 8-17.

53 GFFO. (2022, July 18). Speech by Foreign Minister Annalena Baerbock at the opening of the Petersberg Climate Dialogue. German Federal Foreign Office.

54 Koubi, V. (2019). "Climate Change and Conflict". *Annual Review of Political Science*, 22, 343-360.

55 See Jia, R. (2014). "Weather shocks, sweet potatoes and peasant revolts in historical China". *The Economic Journal*, 92-118; Zhang, D. D., Lee, H. F., Wang, C., Li, B., Pei, Q., Zhang, J., & An, Y. (2011). "The causality analysis of climate change and large-scale human crises". *PNAS*, 17296-17301.

56 See Salehyan, I., & Hendrix, C. S. (2014). "Climate shocks and political violence". *Global Environmental Change*, 28, 239-250.

57 See Ghimire, R., & Ferreira, S. (2015). "Floods and armed conflict". *Environmental and Development Economics*, 21(1), 23-52.

58 See Maystadt, J.-F., & Ecker, O. (2014, March 25). "Extreme Weather and Civil War: Does Drought Fuel Conflict in Somalia through Livestock Price Shocks?" *American Journal of Agricultural Economics*, 96(4), 1157-1182; von Uexkull, N. (2014). "Sustained drought, vulnerability and civil conflict in sub- Saharan Africa". *Political Geography*, 43, 16-26.

59 See Mares, D., & Moffett, K. (2016). "Climate change and interpersonal violence: a "global" estimate and regional inequities". *Climatic Change*, 297-310.

60 See Bellemare, M. F. (2015). "Rising food prices, food price volatility, and social unrest". *American Journal of Agricultural Economics*, 97(1), 1-21.

61 Burke, M. B., Miguel, E., Satyanath, S., Dykema, J. A., & Lobell, D. B. (2009). "Warming increases the risk of civil war in Africa". *PNAS*, 106(49), 20670-20674.

62 Buhaug, H. (2010). "Climate not to blame for African civil wars". PNAS, 107(38), 16477-16482.

63 Selby, J. (2014). "Positivist Climate Conflict Research: A Critique". *Geopolitics*, 19(4), 829-856.

64 This distinction between the two schools has been made by Joshua Busby in Busby, J. W. (2022). *States and Nature. The Effects of Climate Change on Security*. Cambridge: Cambridge University Press. pp.31-2; although important contributions from other scholars are also noted.

65 Based on emissions scenarios set out in the 2000 IPCC Special Report on Emissions Scenarios.

66 See endnote 65.

67 Wallace-Wells, D. (2019). *The Uninhabitable Earth*. New York: Tim Duggan Books.

68 *"Already, climate change has elevated Africa's risk of conflict by more than 10 percent; in that continent, by just 2030, projected temperatures are expected to cause 393,000 additional deaths in battle."* Ibid. p.167.

69 Quoted in Climate Feedback "Scientists explain what New York Magazine article on "The Uninhabitable Earth" gets wrong". Available at: https://climatefeedback.org/evaluation/scientists-explain-what-new-york-magazine-article-on-the-uninhabitable-earth-gets-wrong-david-wallace-wells/

70 Mann, M. E. (2021). *The new climate war: the fight to take back the planet*. New York: Public Affairs, Hatchett Book Group.

71 See endnote 65. p.247.

72 Mach, K. J. et al. (2019). "Climate as a risk factor for armed conflict". *Nature*, 571, 193-197.

73 Bowles, D. C., Butler, C. D., & Morisetti, N. (2015). "Climate change, conflict and health". *Journal of the Royal Society of Medicine*, 390-395.

74 This is an estimate based on the median projections of current policies as of November 2022, as proposed by Climate Action Tracker: https://climateactiontracker.org/

75 See endnote 71.

76 See endnote 18. p.16.

77 von Uexkull, N., & Buhaug, H. (2021). "Security implications of climate change: a decade of scientific progress". *Journal of Peace Research*, 58(1), 3-17. See also: Salehyan, I. (2014). "Climate and Conflict: making sense of disparate findings". *Political Geography*, 1-5.

78 For a discussion on possible institutional reform of the UN to tackle the security implications of climate change, see Sinha-Connolly, L. (2022). "Climate Change and International Security. International Centre for Dialogue Initiatives".

79 Dynes, R. R. (2005). "The Lisbon Earthquake of 1755: The First Modern Disaster". In T. E. Braum, & J. B. Radner, *The Lisbon Earthquake of 1755: Representations and Reactions*. London: Voltaire Foundation.

80 Rousseau, J. J. (1967). "Rousseau to François-Marie Arouet de Voltaire" (Letter 424, 18 August 1756). In J. J. Rousseau, & R. A. Leigh (Ed.), *Complete correspondence of Jean Jacques Rousseau* (Vols. Volume IV 1756-1757, pp. 37-50). Geneva: Institut et Musee Voltaire.

81 Dynes, R. R. (2000). "The Dialogue between Voltaire and Rousseau on the Lisbon Earthquake: The Emergence of a Social Science View". *International Journal of Mass Emergencies and Disasters*, 18(1), 97-115.

82 Karsten Haustein quoted in Muir, M., Bernard, S., & Campbell, C. "Climate graphic of the week: Catastrophic Libyan flooding fuelled by warming oceans". *Financial Times*, 16 September 2023.

83 FT Editorial Board. "Libya's flood disaster was partly man-made". *Financial Times*, 19 September 2023.

84 ND-GAIN. (2021). Somalia. Notre-Dam Global Adaptation Index. Available at: https://gain-new.crc.nd.edu/country/somalia

85 NUPI & SIPRI. (2021, February). "Climate, Peace and Security Fact Sheet: Somalia". This was also corroborated in the 2022 Strategic Review of UNSOM: "the country [is] at the forefront of climate change, [and] the increasing intensity and frequency of climatic shocks are anticipated to exacerbate the humanitarian situation further.... [and also that] climatic changes are likely to increase in both frequency and severity in the upcoming decade."

86 See endnote 59.

87 Rakesh Tikait, leader of BKU Party, quoted in: PTI. "PM Modi should express grief in Parliament over death of 750 farmers during protests: Rakesh Tikait". *The New Indian Express*, 9 October 2021.

88 Wischnath, G., & Buhaug, H. (2014). "Rice or riots: On food production and conflict severity across India". *Political Geography*, 6-15.

89 UNDP. (2020, October 12). "UNDP Climate Security Nexus and Prevention of Violent Extremism". United Nations Development Program.

90 von Lossow, T. (2016). "Water as Weapon: IS on the Euphrates and Tigris". Berlin: Stiftung Wissenschaft und Politik.

91 Quoted in Amnesty International. (2018). "Dead Land. Islamic State's Deliberate Destruction of Iraq's Farmland". London: Amnesty International.

92 Pham-Duc et al. (2020). "The Lake Chad hydrology under current climate change". *Scientific Reports*, 10, 5498.

93 Vivekananda, J., Wall, M., Sylvestre, F., & Nagarajan, C. (2019). "Shoring Up Stability.

Adressing climate and fragility risks in the Lake Chad region". Berlin: adelphi.

94 UNDP. (2017). "Journey to extremism in Africa". New York: United Nations Development Programme.

95 As reported to the UN General Assembly by OHCHR. (2015). "Violations and abuses committed by Boko Haram and the impact on human rights in the countries affected". New York: UNGA.

96 Ibid.

97 IPCC. (2022). "Climate Change 2022: Impacts, Adaptation, and Vulnerability. Contribution of Working Group II to the Sixth Assessment Report of the Intergovernmental Panel on Climate Change. Summary for Policymakers". Cambridge University Press.

98 See Fassihi, F. "Iran Forcefully Clamps Down on Protests Against Growing Water Shortages". *New York Times*, 26 November 2021; Bagchi, D. "Iran vs Afghanistan: Why Helmand water-sharing dispute is boiling over, decades after treaty". *The Print*, 30 May 2023.

99 Tayebi, A. "Iranian President Warns Afghanistan to Abide by Treaty on Water Flows". *Radio Free Europe/ Radio Liberty*, 19 May 2023.

100 von Lossow, T. (2018). "More than Infrastructure: Water Challenges in Iraq". Clingendael.

101 A matter over which the Iraqi government has planned legal action to take to the International Court of Justice. See here: https://www.al-monitor.com/originals/2022/01/iran-iraq-exchange-accusations-over-water-flow

102 Kool, D., Birkman, L., & Torossian, B. (2020). "Interprovincial Water Challenges in Iraq. Working Paper". Water, Peace and Security Partnership.

103 UNDP & UNICEF. (2020). "United Nations Joint Programme Document: Response to Basra water crisis-Iraq. Providing safe drinking water to Basra's population".

104 Human Rights Watch. (2019, July 22). "Iraq: Water Crisis in Basra". Human Rights Watch.

105 See endnote 103.

106 Lackner, H. (2021). "Climate Change and Conflict in Hadhramawt and Al Mahra". Berlin: Berghof Foundation.

107 Friedman, T. "Postcard from Yemen". *New York Times*, 7 May 2013.

108 Quoted in ibid.

109 Small Arms Survey. (2010). "Under Pressure. Social Violence over land and water in Yemen". Yemen Armed Violence Assessment.

110 According to the 2022 estimate from Internal Displacement Monitoring Centre.

111 See endnote 107.

112 Ibid.

113 De Juan, A. (2015). "Long-term environmental change and geographical patterns of violence in Darfur, 2003-2005". *Political Geography*, 45, 22-33.

114 UNEP. (2018, March 21). "How Somalia's charcoal trade is fuelling the Acacia's demise". Available at: https://www.unep.org/news-and-stories/story/how-somalias-charcoal-trade-fuelling-acacias-demise

115 Eklow, K., & Krampe, F. (2019, October). "Climate-related security risks and peacebuilding in Somalia. SIPRI Policy Paper 53". Stockholm International Peace Research Institute.

116 Ibid.

117 UNSOM and OCHR. (2017, December). "Protection of Civilians: Building the Foundation for Peace, Security and Human Rights in Somalia".

118 UNHCR & NRC. (2022, August 11). One million people displaced by drought in Somalia. Available at: https://www.unhcr.org/news/press/2022/8/62f4c3894/million-people-displaced-drought- somalia.html#:~:text=More%20than%20755%2C000%20people%20have,Norwegian%20Refugee%20Co uncil%20(NRC)

119 UNEP, UN Women, UNDP and UNDPPA/PBSO. (2020, June 11). "Gender, Climate & Security. Sustaining inclusive peace on the frontlines of climate change".

120 Ibid.

121 Witsenburg, K., & Roba, A. W. (2004). *Surviving pastoral decline: pastoral sedentarisation, natural resource management and livelihood diversification in Marsabit District*, Northern Kenya. Deel: Vol.1. Amsterdam.

122 See endnote 1. p.404.

123 Africa Center for Strategic Studies. (2019, August 08). "Mitigating Farmer-Herder Violence in Mali". Available at: https://africacenter.org/spotlight/mitigating-farmer-herder-violence-in-mali/

124 Michel, D. (2021). "Climate Security, Conflict Prevention, and Peacebuilding". Carnegie Europe.

125 Ibid.

126 See endnote 95.

127 UN. (2022, September 25). "High-level independent panel on security and development in crisis-torn Sahel region launched at UN". Available at: https://news.un.org/en/story/2022/09/1127931

128 "The surprising upside of climate migration". *The Economist*, 1 July 2023.

129 See Burke, J. "Niger's coup adds to chaos in the Sahel, but it may also offer some hope". *The Guardian*, 6 August 2023; Burke, J. (2020, October 19). "Sahel region is 'canary in the coalmine' on climate, says UN official". *The Guardian*, 19 October 2020.

130 Fletcher, T. (2022). *Ten Survival Skills for a World in Flux*. London: William Collins. p.140

131 Quoted in Wintour, P. "UK minister seeks cross-party support for bold roadmap on development goals". *The Guardian*, 19 July 2023.

132 Email exchange between the author and Johnny West, Lead Architect, Global Registry of Fossil Fuels, Berlin, July 2023.

133 Xu, C., Kohler, T. A., Lenton, T. M., Svenning, J.-C., & Scheffer, M. (2020, May). "Future of the human climate niche". *PNAS*, 117(21), 11350-11355.

134 Battisti, D. S., & Naylor, R. L. (2009). "Historical Warnings of Future Food Insecurity with Unprecedented Seasonal Heat". *Science*, 240-244.

135 "How cities can respond to extreme heat". *The Economist*, 20 July 2023.

136 Goodell, J. (2023). *The Heat Will Kill You First*. Boston MA: Little, Brown and Company.

137 May, T. "Extreme Weather Hits China with Massive Floods and Scorching Heat". *New York Times*, 23 June 2022.

138 "India's deadly heatwaves are getting even hotter". *The Economist*, 2 April 2023; Parkin, B., & Hodgson, C. "Rebuilding Pakistan: how much should rich nations help?" *Financial Times*, 8 March 2023.

139 UNHCR. (2022, May 23). "UNHCR: Ukraine, other conflicts push forcibly displaced total over 100 million for first time". Available at: https://www.unhcr.org/news/press/2022/5/628a389e4/unhcr-ukraine-other-conflicts-push-forcibly-displaced-total-100-million.html

140 McKibben, B. (2022, October 6). *Where will we live?* New York Review of Books.

141 IDMC. (2023). "Global Report on Internal Displacement 2023. Internal Displacement and Food Security". Geneva: Internal Displacement Monitoring Centre.

142 Institute for Economics and Peace. (2020, September 9). "Over one billion people at threat of being displaced by 2050 due to environmental change, conflict and civil unrest". Available at: https://www.economicsandpeace.org/wp-content/uploads/2020/09/Ecological-Threat-Register-Press-Release-27.08-FINAL.pdf

143 See endnote 129.

144 World Meteorological Organisation. (2021, May 27). "New climate predictions increase likelihood of temporarily reaching 1.5°C in next 5 years". Available at: https://public.wmo.int/en/media/press-release/new-climate-predictions-increase-likelihood-of-temporarily-reaching-15-%C2%B0c-next-5=

145 Reuveny, R. (2007). "Climate change-induced migration and violent conflict". *Political Geography*, 26(6), 656-673.

146 Bhavani, R. R., & Lacina, B. (2015). "The effects of weather-induced migration on sons of the soil riots in India". *World Politics*, 67, 760-794.

147 Al Jazeera "Kerry hopes climate cooperation can redefine US-China ties". *Al Jazeera*, 18 July 2023.

148 See endnote 78.

149 Koubi, V., Bohmelt, T., Spilker, G., & Schaffer, L. (2018). "The Determinants of Environmental Migrants' Conflict Perception". *International Organisation*, 72(4), 905-936.

150 For analysis of the contributory factors in the Brexit vote, see Clarke, H. D., Goodwin, M., & Whitely, P. (2017). *Brexit: Why Britain voted to leave the European Union*. Cambridge: Cambridge University Press.

151 See endnote 141.

152 Speakman Cordall, S. "Water ban on drought-stricken Tunisia adds to growing crisis". *The Guardian*, 5 April 2023.

153 Chrisafis, A., & O'Carroll, L. "Pope Francis decries 'fanaticism of indifference' over migration". *The Guardian*, 22 September 2023.

154 IOM. (2015). "Migrants Caught in Crisis: The IOM Experience in Libya". Geneva: International Organisation for Migration.

155 Ibid.

156 Werz, M., & Hoffman, M. (2016). "Europe's Twenty-first Century Challenge: Climate Change, Migration and Security". *European View*, 15(1), 145-154.

157 Zlobin, A. (2020, June 04). Крупнейшая катастрофа в Арктике: что известно о разливе топлива под Норильском. Forbes.ru. Available at: https://www.forbes.ru/obshchestvo-photogallery/402193-krupneyshaya-katastrofa-v-arktike-chto-izvestno-o-razlive-topliva

158 Lustgarten, A. "How Russia Wins the Climate Crisis". *New York Times*, 16 December 2020.

159 Krampe, F., & de Coning, C. (2021, December 13). "Does Russia's Veto Mean Climate Security Is Off the Security Council Agenda?" Available at: https://theglobalobservatory.org/2021/12/russia-veto-climate-security-off-security-council-agenda

160 Quoted in Belton, C. "Putin thinks West will blink first in war of attrition, Russian elites say". *Washington Post*, 3 June 2022.

161 The White House. (2021). "Report on the Impact of Climate Change Migration". Washington: The White House. p.10.

162 El-Hinnawi, E. (1985). "Environmental Refugees". Nairobi: UNEP.

163 Riley, T. "Just 100 companies responsible for 71% of global emissions, study says". *The Guardian*, 10 July 2017.

164 ten Hove, D. (2021, August 1). "The UN Refugee Agency's Bold Plan to Manage the Crisis of Climate Migrants". Available at: https://www.passblue.com/2021/08/01/the-un-refugee-agencys-bold-plan-to-manage-the-crisis-of-climate-migrants/

165 UNHCR. (2021, October 1). "Legal considerations regarding claims for international protection made in the context of the adverse effects of climate change and disasters".

166 See Rodríguez-Garavito, C. (2022). *Litigating the Climate Emergency: How Human Rights, Courts, and Legal Mobilization Can Bolster Climate Action*. Cambridge: Cambridge University Press.

167 Dempster, H., & Ober, K. (2020, January 20). "New Zealand's "Climate Refugee" Visas: Lessons for the Rest of the World". *Center for Global Development*. Available at: https://www.cgdev.org/blog/new- zealands-climate-refugee-visas-lessons-rest-world

168 Schloss, C. (2022). "The Role of Environmental Disasters in Asylum Cases: Do German Courts Take Disasters into Account?" In S. Behrman, & A. Kent (Eds.), *Climate Refugees: Global, Local and Critical Approaches* (pp. 261-276). Cambridge: Cambridge University Press.

169 Leatherby, L. "How a Vast Demographic Shift Will Reshape the World". *New York Times*, 16 July 2023.

170 Vince, G. (2022). *Nomad Century: How to Survive the Climate Upheaval*. London: Allen Lane. See also reviews: Ward, B. "Nomad Century: How to Survive the Climate Upheaval by Gaia Vince review – a world without borders". The Guardian, 14 August 2022; Ahuja, A. "Nomad Century by Gaia Vince — acclimatising to crisis". Financial Times, 23 August 2022; Simon, S. "'Nomad Century' delivers a message that's sharp and jolting about mankind's future". *NPR*, 27 August 2022; ABC News. "New book makes argument for addressing climate migration". *ABC News*, 22 August 2022.

171 For a particularly useful analysis of these topics, see Parr, A. (2022). "Making the Important Urgent. Can climate migration light up the slow-burn politics of the climate emergency?" Oxford Smith School of Enterprise and the Environment.

172 For more information on the project see: https://www.links-nigeria.com/climate-smart-agriculture/

173 "The global rice crisis". *The Economist*, 28 March 2023.

174 Uphoff, N. (2022). "Applications of SRI and methods in areas of disrupted agriculture". In N. Uphoff, *The System of Rice Intensification: Memoires of an Innovation*. Ithaca, New York.

175 Orenstein, M. (2023). "Putin the Green? The Unintended Consequences of Russia's Energy War on Europe". Philadelphia: Foreign Policy Research Institute.

176 Sager, L. (2022, March). "The Global Consumer Incidence of Carbon Pricing: Evidence from Trade". Georgetown University.

177 Milne, R. "Greta Thunberg accuses Norway of 'green colonialism' over wind farm". *Financial Times*, 27 February 2023.

178 Feldman, E. "Climate Activists Throw Soup on Vincent van Gogh's 'Sunflowers' to Protest Fossil Fuels". *Smithsonian Magazine*, 17 October 2022.

179 Joint Committee on Human Rights. (2022).

"Legislative Scrutiny: Public Order Bill". London: UK Parliament. See also Ahmed, Y. (2022, December 14). "UK Should Protect the Rights to Protest and Strike, not Undermine Them". Available at: https://www.hrw.org/news/2022/12/14/uk-should-protect-rights-protest-and-strike-not-undermine-them

180 Gayle, D. "Climate diplomacy is hopeless, says author of How to Blow Up a Pipeline". *The Guardian*, 21 April 2023.

181 Monbiot, G. "The hard right and climate catastrophe are intimately linked. This is how". *The Guardian*, 15 June 2023.

182 Priestley, C. (2020). "The Peacebuilding Implications of Energy Transitions to a Carbon-Neutral Future". Geneva: Quaker United Nations Office.

183 See Hall, N. "No Water Wars?" (2023, June 26) and "Earth Day: Lessons for Environmental Cooperation" (2023, April 24). *Center for Strategic & International Studies*. Available at: https://www.csis.org/

184 "The Challenge of the Age: The world has to adapt to the climate change it will not avoid". *The Economist*, 1 November 2022.

185 See endnote 183.

186 Soffiantini, G. (2020). "Food insecurity and political instability during the Arab Spring". *Global Food Security*, 26, 100400.

187 Werrell, C. E., Femia, F., & Sternburg, T. (2015). "Did we see it coming? State fragility, climate vulnerability, and the uprisings in Syria and Egypt". *SAIS Review of International Affairs*, 35(1), 29-46.

188 Brown, O., & Keating, M. (2015). "Addressing Natural Resource Conflict". London: Chatham House.

189 Ross, M. L. (2015). "What Have We Learned about the Resource Curse?" *Annual Review of Political Science*, 18, 239-59.

190 See Overland, I. (2019, March). "The geopolitics of renewable energy: Debunking four emerging myths". Energy Research and Social Science, 49, 36-40. Some symptoms of the resource curse, however, may endure, particularly in the case of solar energy production; see Brunet, C. et al. (2022). "Will solar energy escape the natural "resource curse"?" *Energy Strategy Reviews*, 44, 101010.

191 Owen, W. (2022, January 17). "Rystad Energy: Copper supply deficit threatens renewables and EVs as investment lags demand". *Global Mining Review*. Available at: https://www.globalminingreview.com/mining/17012022/rystad-energy-copper-supply-deficit-threatens-renewables-and-evs-as-investment-lags-demand/

192 Fastmarkets. "Lithium supply and demand to 2030". Available at: https://www.fastmarkets.com/insights/lithium-supply-and-demand-to-2030

193 Dixon, H. "Old Cold War tool could help in new era of tension". *Reuters*, 27 July 2023.

194 Alves Dias, P., Blagoeva, D., Pavel, C. & Aranitidis, N. (2018). "Cobalt: demand-supply balances in the transition to electric mobility". Luxembourg: Joint Research Centre. Science for Policy Report. European Commission.

195 Hook, L., Dempsey, H., & Nugent, C. "The new commodity superpowers". *Financial Times*, 8 August 2023.

196 According to the Fragile State Index 2022 (https://fragilestatesindex.org/) and Transparency International.

197 Amnesty International and Afrewatch. (2016). ""This is what we die for". Human Rights Abuse in the Democratic Republic of Congo Power the Global Trade in Cobalt". London: Amnesty International.

198 Data retrieved from World Bank.

199 OPEC. (2021). "Saudi Arabia Facts and Figures". Available at: https://www.opec.org/opec_web/en/about_us/169.htm

200 Al Jazeera. "Saudi Arabia to impose 'painful' austerity measures, triple VAT". *Al Jazeera*, 11 May 2020.

201 Raval, A., Cornish, C., & Munshi, N. "Net-zero's high price for fossil fuel economies". *Financial Times*, 27 May 2021.

202 Ibid.

203 Al Jazeera. "Fuel subsidy cut will save Nigeria but impose burden". *Al Jazeera*, 12 June 2023.

204 Todman, W. (2023). "Powering Recovery. Reform, Reconstruction, and Renewables in Conflict-Affected States in the Arab World". Washington DC: CSIS.

205 Ibid.

206 "Why Africa is poised to become a big player in energy markets". *The Economist*, 18 July 2023.

207 See endnote 183.

208 UNSOS. (2020, October 26). "Baidoa set to boost renewable energy production". Available at: https://unsos.

unmissions.org/baidoa-set-boost-renewable-energy-production

209 Druet, D., Lyammouri, R., & Mozersky, D. (2021). "From Renewable Energy to Peacebuilding in Mali. MINUSMA's Opportunity to Bridge the Gap". Stimson Center and Energy Peace Partners.

210 Ibid.

211 See endnote 204.

212 Ibid.

213 Prime Minister's Office. (2021, November 13). Glasgow Climate Pact keeps critical 1.5C global warming goal alive. UK Government. Available at: https://www.gov.uk/government/news/pm-glasgow-climate-pact-keeps-critical-15c-global-warming-goal-alive

214 For a full definition used in 2022 IPCC 6th Assessment Report: "In human systems, the process of adjustment to actual or expected climate and its effects, in order to moderate harm or exploit beneficial opportunities. In natural systems the process of adjustment to actual climate and its effects; human intervention may facilitate adjustment to expected climate."

215 Abshir, S. (2023). "The Challenges of Climate Financing in Conflict Contexts". Brussels: European Institute for Peace.

216 O'Connor, A.-M. "This Palestinian village had solar power - until Israeli soldiers took it away". *Washington Post*, 7 July 2017. See also UN-ESCWA. (2022, October) Countering economic dependence and de-development in the occupied Palestinian territory. Beirut: UN-ESCWA.

217 See endnote 18.

218 Ibid.

219 Campbell, I. (2011). "Conflict sensitive approaches to local climate change adaptation in Nepal". London: Saferworld.

220 See endnote 1. p.583. See also Vidal, J. "Norman Borlaug: humanitarian hero or menace to society?" The Guardian, 1 April 2014.

221 Dabelko, G. D., Herzer Risi, L., Null, S., Parker, M., & Sticklor, R. (2013). "Backdraft: The Conflict Potential of Climate Change Adaptation and Mitigation". Environmental Change and Security Program. Wilson Center.

222 Climate Security Expert Network. (2019). "Climate-Fragility Risk Factsheet. Afghanistan". Berlin: Climate Security Expert Network.

223 According to the ND-GAIN index measuring climate vulnerability and readiness to adapt. Accessed at: https://gain.nd.edu/our-work/country-index/

224 Krampe, F., Smith, E. S., & Hamidi, M. D. (2021). "Security implications of climate development in conflict-affected states implications of local-level effects of rural hydropower development on farmers in Herat". *Political Geography*, 90.

225 Krampe, F., Hegazi, F., & VanDeever, S. (2021). "Sustaining peace through better resource governance: Three potential mechanisms for environmental peacebuilding". *World Development*, 144.

226 55% as reported by rural communities in: Oxfam. (2009). "The Cost of War - Afghan experiences of conflict - 1978-2009". Kabul: Oxfam.

227 See endnote 225.

228 Ibid, citing a local news report, accessed at: https://youtu.be/OK7j7dTmzPA

229 Glover, J. "*Kajaki Dam: Contentious, costly and a failure*". The Guardian, 4 September 2008.

230 UNCCD. (2020). "The Great Green Wall. Press Kit". Bonn: United Nations Convention to Combat Desertification.

231 Bove, T. (2021, March 24). "The Great Green Wall is Failing, But its Legacy Could Still Be A Success". Earth. Available at: https://earth.org/the-great-green-wall-legacy/

232 Rechtschaffen, D. (2017, September 18). "How China's Growing Deserts Are Choking The Country". Forbes. Available at: forbes.com/sites/danielrechtschaffen/2017/09/18/how-chinas-growing-deserts-are-choking-the-country/

233 "Great Green Wall. Vast tree-planting in arid regions is failing to halt the desert's march". *The Economist*, 23 August 2014.

234 Mohammad Bakarr of the Global Environment Facility, quoted in Morrison, J. "The "Great Green Wall" Didn't Stop Desertificaiton, But It Evolved Into Something That Might". *Smithsonian Magazine*, 23 August 2016.

235 UNCCD. (n.d.). Great Green Wall Initiative: Impact. United Nations Convention to Combat Desertification. Available at: https://www.unccd.int/our-work/ggwi/impact

236 Kalilou, O. (2021). "Climate change and conflict in the Sahel: the acacia gum tree as a tool for environmental peacebuilding". *International Affairs*, 201-218.

237 UNCTAD. (2018). "Commodities at a Glance: Special Issue on Gum Arabic". Geneva: United Nations Conference on Trade and Development.

238 World Bank. (2005). "Burkina Faso: The Zaï Technique and Enhanced Agricultural Productivity". Washington D.C.: World Bank.

239 Mitchell, C., & Alpha, K. "Africa's dream of a Great Green Wall wilts in the desert". *Sunday Times*, 12 March 2023.

240 Pandey, N., Ruttinger, L., & Wolfmaier, S. (2020). "Climate Fragility Risk Brief: Nepal". Berlin: adelphi.

241 Ibid.

242 Nightingale, A. J. (2018, April). "Nepal's Towering Climate Adaptation Challenges". *Current History*, 117(798), 135-141.

243 See endnote 241.

244 Hovden, A. "If this is what a small glacial lake flood can do, imagine a big one". *Nepali Times*, August 2011.

245 See endnote 241.

246 See Shrestha, M. L., & Shrestha, A. B. (2004). "Recent Trends and Climate Change Impacts on Glacier Retreat/Glacier Lakes in Nepal and Potential Adaptation Measures". Paris: OECD. Also: Alam, M., & Regmi, B. R. (2004). "Nepal: Capacity Strengthening in the Least Developed Countries for Adaptation to Climate Change". Dhaka: BCAS and IIED.

247 See endnote 243. p.137.

248 Ibid.

249 See endnote 243.

250 Ibid.

251 See Vivekananda, J., Schilling, J., & Smith, D. (2014). "Understanding Resilience in Climate Change and Conflict Affected Regions of Nepal". *Geopolitics*, 19(4), 911-936; Zala, B. (2012). "Water Scarcity: the Real and Virtual Problems". Zurich: ETH Zurich.

252 Bhandari, A., Thakuri, S., Koirala, P., & Devkota, M. P. (2021, December). "Conflict-Sensitive Climate Change Adaptation in Nepal: An Analysis of Climate Resilience Policy Frameworks". *Journal of Forest and Livelihood*, 20(1), 31-44. Bhandari et al. also point to the missed opportunity of leveraging these initiatives for peacebuilding.

253 See endnote 243.

254 For a similar example from India relating to the distribution of water and subsequent scarcity, see Lyla, M. (2007). "Whose scarcity? Whose property? The case of water in western India". *Land Use Policy*, 24(4), 654-663.

255 See endnote 243.

256 Zierler, D. (2011). *The Invention of Ecocide: Agent Orange, Vietnam, and the Scientists Who Changed the Way We Think About the Environment*. University of Georgia Press.

257 United States Senate Hearing 93rd Congress. (1974 January 25 & March 20). "Weather modification: hearings before the Subcommittee on Oceans and International Environment of the Committee on Foreign Relations, Ninety-third Congress, second session, on the need for an international agreement prohibiting the use of environmental and geophysical modification as weapons of war and briefing on department of defense weather modification activity". Available at: https://www.govinfo.gov/app/details/CHRG-93shrg295440

258 Conca, K., & Dabelko, G. D. (2002). *Environmental Peacemaking*. Baltimore: Woodrow Wilson Center with Johns Hopkins University Press. p.9.

259 Such as Kaplan, R. D. (1994, February). "The Coming Anarchy". *Atlantic Monthly*, 273(2), 44-76; and Homer-Dixon, T. (1999). Environmental Scarcity and Violence. Princeton: Princeton University Press.

260 Ide, T., Bruch, C., Carius, A., Conca, K., Dabelko, G. D., Matthew, R., & Weinthal, E. (2021). "The past and future(s) of environmental peacebuilding". *International Affairs*, 97(1), 1-16. pp.2-3.

261 Krampe, F. (2017). "Toward Sustainable Peace: A New Research Agenda for Post-Conflict Natural Resource Management". *Global Environmental Politics*, 17(8), 1-8.

262 See endnote 204. Also: Williams, A., & Sevastopulo, D. "John Kerry visits Beijing to restart stalled US-China climate talks". *Financial Times*, 16 July 2023.

263 Boyes, R. "The first water war is uncomfortably close". *The Times*, 27 July 2021.

264 EcoPeace Middle East. (2016). "Community Based Problem Solving on Water Issues. Cross-border "Priority Initiatives" of the Good Water Neighbours Project". Tel Aviv: EcoPeace Middle East.

265 Friends of the Earth Middle East. (2013). "'Good Water Neighors' Final Program Report". Tel Aviv: Friends of the Earth Middle East.

266 Ibid.

267 EcoPeace Middle East. (2015). Good Water Neighbours Project. Available at: https://panorama.solutions/sites/default/files/gwn_project_overview_updated_july_2015_1.pdf

268 Mansour, H., & Reiffenstuel, A. (2022). "The Jordan, Israel, and UAE Water-for-Energy Deal: Potential and Pitfalls of Energy and Water Sharing-Agreements in the Middle East". Amman: Konrad Adenauer Stiftung.

269 Ide, T. (2020). "The dark side of environmental peacebuilding". *World Development*, 127, 1-21.

270 Ibid.

271 Ibid. p.7.

272 Cyprus Institute. (n.d.). Climate Change and Impact. Available at: https://www.cyi.ac.cy/index.php/eewrc/eewrc-research-projects/climate-change-and-impact.html#:~:text=Given%20the%20ongoing%20decrease%20in,the%202020%20to%202050%20period

273 Hadjimichael, M., & Papastylianou, K. (2019). "Environmental Protection and Cooperation in an (Ethnically) Divided Island: the Case of Cyprus". Oslo: PRIO. p.55.

274 Akçalı, E., & Antonsich, M. (2009). "'Nature Knows No Boundaries': A Critical Reading of UNDP Environmental Peacemaking in Cyprus". *Annals of the Association of American Geographers*, 99(5), 940- 947.

275 Ibid. p.945.

276 See endnote 270.

277 Burt, M., & Keiru, B. J. (2011). "Strengthening post-conflict peacebuilding through community water-resource management: case studies from Democratic Republic of Congo, Afghanistan and Liberia". *Water International*, 36(2), 232-241.

278 Ibid. p.234.

279 Ibid.

280 Ibid.

281 Ibid.

282 See endnote 22. p.37.

283 "Herders and farmers seek reasons for east Africa's drought". *The Economist* 17 August 2023.

284 Selig, K., & Guskin, E. "You're doing it wrong: Recycling and other myths about tackling climate change". *Washington Post*, 28 August 2023.

285 K.C., S. (2013). "Community Vulnerability to Floods and Landslides in Nepal". *Ecology and Society*, 18(1).

286 Striessnig, E., Lutz, W., & Patt, A. G. (2013). "Effects of Educational Attainment on Climate Risk Vulnerability". *Ecology and Society*, 18(1).

287 Quoted from her article in *The Economist*: "Vanessa Nakate on how girls' education can help solve the climate crisis". *The Economist*, 8 March 2022.'

288 For more information about the project, see: https://berghof-foundation.org/work/projects/somalia-i4p-and-inclusive-dialogue-in-galmudug-state

289 See endnote 22. p.32.

290 Ibid. p.38.

291 UNDPPA. (2022). "The Implications of Climate Change for Mediation and Peace Processes. DPPA Practice Note". New York: United Nations Department of Political and Peacebuilding Affairs.

292 Ibid. p.14.

293 Brodzinsky, S. "Deforestation soars in Colombia after Farc rebels' demobilization". *The Guardian*, 11 July 2017.

294 Sax, S. "Peace: A new tool for reducing deforestation in the Colombian Amazon". *Mongabay*, 18 July 2023. See also: Taylor, L. "Colombia deforestation plummets as peace efforts focus on rainforest". *The Guardian*, 12 July 2023.

295 See endnote 292. p.17.

296 Vatikiotis, M. (2022, August 08). "Mediation to mitigate the human cost of climate change". Speech at the Aranda Mediation Conference.

297 HD. (2021). "Agro-pastoral mediation in the Sahel". Geneva: Centre for Humanitarian Dialogue.

298 Hall, N. (2023, April 24). "Earth Day: Lessons for Environmental Cooperation". *Center for Strategic and International Studies*.

299 Stein, J., & Birnbaum, M. "The war in Ukraine is a human tragedy. It's also an environmental disaster". *Washington Post*, 13 March 2023.

300 See Mundy, V. "Ukraine's 'hero river' helped save Kyiv. But what now for its newly restored wetlands?" *The Guardian*, 11 May 2022. Also: Mundy, V. "WarWilding: a new word to describe the startling effects of using nature as a weapon". *The Guardian*, 5 September 2022.

301 Ibid.

302 Perga, T. "Ecocide in Ukraine: How Russia's War

Will Poison The Country (And Europe) For Decades To Come". *De Gruyter: Conversations*, 30 June 2022. See also: Wengle, S., & Dankevych, V. "Kakhovka Dam breach in Ukraine caused economic, agricultural and ecological devastation that will last for years". *The Conversation*, 7 July 2023.

303 WWF; BCG. (2023). "A Sustainable Economic Recovery for People and Nature". World Wildlife Fund and Boston Consulting Group.

304 CBD. (2023). Country Profile Ukraine - Main Details. Available at: https://www.cbd.int/countries/profile/?country=ua#:~:text=Occupying%20less%20than%206%25%20of,r

305 Andrushchenko, S. "A new tool could make Russia pay for environmental damage in Ukraine". *Financial Times*, 12 April 2023. Also: Sandbu, M. "Ukraine's rapid reconstruction will be in Europe's own interest". *Financial Times*, 4 July 2023.

306 Falkner, R. (2023). "Weaponised Energy and Climate Change: Assessing Europe's Response to the Ukraine War". *LSE Public Policy Review*, 3(1).

307 Hancock, A. "UN pushes EU to help fund Ukraine's post-war clean-up". *Financial Times*, 19 June 2023.

308 See endnote 307.

309 Outlook India. "Explained: What Jaishankar Said About Europe, Why Germany Chancellor Praises Him". *Outlook India*, 20 February 2023.

310 Financial Times. "A spiralling cycle of violence in the West Bank". *Financial Times*, 27 June 2023. See also: Ero, C. (2023, March 22). "Global Politics in the Shadow of Ukraine". International Crisis Group. Available at: https://www.crisisgroup.org/global-ukraine/global-politics-shadow-ukraine; Feltman, J. "War, peace, and the international system after Ukraine". *Brookings*, 28 March 2023.

311 Cliffe, J. "The war that changed the world". *New Statesman*, 17 August 2022.

312 Tharoor, I. "Global hunger enters a grim 'new normal'". *Washington Post*, 17 July 2023.

313 Milne, R. "Arctic chill: western nations fear China and Russia will exploit regional tensions". *Financial Times*, 5 June 2023.

314 See endnote 307.

315 Coles et al. (2023, February 20). "Seven ways Russia's war on Ukraine has changed the world". Chatham House. Available at: https://www.chathamhouse.org/2023/02/seven-ways-russias-war-ukraine-has-changed-world

316 See endnote 176.

317 Allison, G. "China's dominance of solar poses difficult choices for the west". *Financial Times*, 22 June 2023.

318 Muir, M. "Renewable energy drive to lift capacity by a third in 2023, IEA says". *Financial Times*, 1 June 2023.

319 Dixon, H. "Ukraine has more pluses than minuses for climate". *Reuters Breakingviews*, 26 September 2022.

320 See endnote 176.

321 Way, R., Ives, M. C., Mealy, P., & Farmer, J. D. (2022, September 13). "Empirically grounded technology forecasts and the energy transition". *Joule*, 6, 1-26.

322 Gelles, D. "The War in Ukraine Upended Energy Markets. What Does That Mean for the Climate?" *New York Times*, 14 January 2023.

323 Plokhy, S. (2021). *The Gates of Europe: a History of Ukraine*. New York: Basic Books. p.260.

324 Snyder, T. (2015). *Black earth: the Holocaust as history and warning*. Tim Duggan Books. For review, see: Evans, R. J. "Black Earth by Timothy Snyder review – a new lesson to be learned from the Holocaust". The Guardian, 10 September 2015.

325 Koch, A., Brierly, C., Maslin, M. M., & Lewis, S. L. (2019). "Earth system impacts of the European arrival and Great Dying in the Americas after 1492". *Quaternary Science Reviews*, 207, 13-36.

326 See endnote 1. pp.350-1.

327 See endnote 292. p.5.

328 Carrington, D. "Rising seas threaten 'mass exodus on a biblical scale', UN chief warns". *The Guardian*, 14 February 2023.

329 Marshall, T. (2021). *The Power of Geography: Ten Maps that Reveal the Future of Our World*. London: Elliott and Thompson.

330 Makortoff, K. "UK could face 'banking crisis worse than 2008' if City fails to prepare for fossil fuel collapse". *The Guardian*, 12 January 2023.

331 See endnote 1. p.369.

332 See endnote 1. p.554.

333 Bosch, T., & Vinke, K. (2022). "Integrating Climate in Germany's National Security Strategy". Berlin: DGAP .

334 Jones, O. "Think Sunak's anti-refugee stance is bad? Just

wait till the climate crisis truly ravages poorer countries". *The Guardian*, 6 March 2023.

335 See endnote 98. pp.13-14.

336 Hodgson, C. "Horn of Africa drought made 100 times more likely by climate change, scientists report". *Financial Times*, 27 April 2023.

337 Williams, A. "World Bank to 'stretch every dollar' with new lending measures". *Financial Times*, 18 July 2023.

338 See endnote 22.

339 Data retrieved from Our World in Data, accessed 19 April 2022: https://ourworldindata.org/grapher/share-of-cumulative-co2?time=latest&country=~SOM

340 "Drought killed 43,000 people in Somalia last year". *The Economist*, 23 March 2023.

341 Brown, G. "Rich nations have promised to pay for the climate crisis – but will they?" *The Guardian*, 26 November 2022.

342 Private email exchange with Jay Collins, Vice Chairman, Citibank. 3 October 2023.

343 Lakhani, N. "Fossil fuel firms owe climate reparations of $209bn a year, says study". *The Guardian*, 19 May 2023.

344 See for instance Isabella Kaminski, "Why 2023 will be a watershed year for climate litigation", *The Guardian*, 4 January 2023

345 Professor Lavanja Rajmani, quoted in Hodgson, C. "Top UN court to assess countries' climate obligations after resolution passes". *Financial Times*, 29 March 2023.

346 Redfearn, G., & Morton, A. "'Climate villain': scientists say Rupert Murdoch wielded his media empire to sow confusion and doubt". *The Guardian*, 23 September 2023.

347 Clark, P. "The fossil fuel industry will not lead us out of the climate crisis". *Financial Times*, 19 July 2023.

348 Hodgson, C. "The money behind the coming wave of climate litigation". Financial Times, 5 June 2023. See also: Kaminski, I. "Big polluters' share prices fall after climate lawsuits, study finds". The Guardian, 22 May 2023; Kaminski, I. "Lawsuits are key tool in delivering climate justice, says UN body". *The Guardian*, 27 July 2023.

Berghof Foundation

We thank the Ministry for Foreign Affairs of Finland and the Swiss Federal Department of Foreign Affairs for their generous support for this publication.

Berghof Foundation
Operations gGmbH
Lindenstr. 34
10969 Berlin
Germany

www.berghof-foundation.org
info@berghof-foundation.org

Research support and content editing:
Tom Breese

Process coordination:
Annett Rößling

Design:
VerbalVisual
www.verbalvisu.al

Printing:
TJ Books
www.tjbooks.co.uk

MIX
Paper from responsible sources
FSC® C013056
www.fsc.org

Klimaneutral
Druckprodukt
ClimatePartner.com/10884-2205-1006

Published by:
Berghof Foundation Operations gGmbH
ISBN: 978-3-941514-63-8

Distributed in the UK by Turnaround Publisher Services www.turnaround-uk.com